True Confections

or
How my family arranged my marriage

a novel by
Sondra Gotlieb

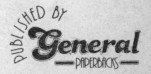

PUBLISHED BY

General

PAPERBACKS

A Division of General Publishing Co. Ltd.
Don Mills, Ontario

First published in 1978 by
Musson Book Company,
a division of
General Publishing Co. Ltd.

General Paperback Edition published December, 1980

ISBN 0-7736-7004-1

Printed and bound in Canada

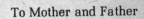

To Mother and Father

Prologue

Once upon a time in a flat cold city, colder than Moscow or Propoisk, it was believed that all people should marry.

The city was Winnipeg, in Canada, and, when I lived there twenty-five years ago, the belief was strongest in the north end of the city.

In Moscow or Propoisk during the 1850s, marriages were arranged by the parents. It was not considered necessary for the bride and groom to know each other before the wedding.

In Winnipeg during the 1950s (there was no Winnipeg in the 1850s) it was more difficult for parents to arrange marriages. The myth of romantic love and courtship had spread north from Hollywood and influenced the young. But if the families were determined, yet subtle enough, even to the point of trickery, it was still possible to arrange a marriage. Especially if the girl was young and lacking confidence.

I was eighteen when I married and I did not choose my husband.

But it was not like in Moscow or Propoisk a hundred years ago when a marriage was planned and a couple matched without fuss except for dowry complications. In my case there were false starts and backtracking. I was pushed one way and another by my relations, parents, and friends. I wasn't a docile girl and if manipulation became too obvious I would sulk and disobey. But everything and everybody I knew pointed me toward marriage.

This story is about my arranged marriage and how it came to be.

It is also about the kind of world where such an anachronism could occur. All my mother's friends believed their most important job was cooking for the family. Another anachronism which goes well with the first.

True Confections

1
The
Hump

Mother always gave me what I wanted.

At my sweet sixteen party there was a long layered sandwich loaf, iced with cream cheese and olives, six girlfriends, three of them named Carol, and no boys. Mother had spent two days in the kitchen making the Cream Cheese Surprise, Melting Moments (sugared almond shortbreads), and Russian Butter Cake, all special requests from the birthday girl.

Mother's attitude was impeccable — she didn't remind me about my weight and only once suggested that I ask boys.

But my father was dissatisfied with my party arrangements. He pointed out that one of the Carols, the most popular, had just given a semi-formal sweet sixteen, mixed, and said I should do the same.

"What are you afraid of, Verna? Have boys. Just don't criticize them, then the boys will go after you like they go after Carol. Don't worry about your weight. Plump is good."

My father believed in the old Eastern European maxim: "When you marry a daughter a hump is off your back."

And he knew what kind of girls married quickest. Delicate figures and elegant profiles attract triflers who want a showpiece to flaunt but not to marry. Fat arms and full cheeks will not bring in the quantity. But they appeal to the steady, shrewd male who suspects that too slender a waist, too intense a look, could mean an inward, selfish disposition.

"Good skin is the most important thing a girl can have," father said. "And you have less pimples than the Carols or Normas."

My disposition, however, wasn't as serene as my solid appearance might lead men to believe. I used to criticize my father all the time about everything and would jump up and leave the dinner table when he complained to my mother.

"Fanny, this meat isn't well done. Food has to be well cooked to get rid of germs. God knows who's handled it — the men in the abbatoir . . . I read in the newspaper they had to get rid of one because he was a typhoid carrier . . . and LeFeel, that schlepper of a butcher who never washes his hands even when he goes to the toilet."

The worry over undercooked food was one of my father's old standbys. It always irritated me because I liked rare meat, was prudish and disliked his reference to toilets, and knew that my father only spoke from hearsay evidence about the butcher's hygiene. My brother, Ronnie, who picked up the meat at the shop and liked to tease, once told my father that there was no time span between the moment the butcher flushed the toilet and cut the beef.

When I really wanted to get my father angry, I remained at the table and told him I intended to leave home when I finished high school and go to Alberta or New York. "I feel stifled," I used to say.

To prove my point I would walk the length of Portage Avenue and loiter about Millie Moss Travel, hoping she would let me look at a brochure.

Millie didn't like me hanging around. Only on her calmer days would she hand over a glossy leaflet with the Statue of Liberty or Jasper Lodge on the front. She made me swear on the heads of my parents that I wouldn't take them out of her place.

Was it possible that New York or Banff had something to do with me? I used to read every word on the brochures, looking for a sign of my future in the blurb, wondering if my picture would ever be taken as a waving tourist in the eye of Liberty, or picking poppies in a tweed skirt on the slopes of Lake Louise.

The idea of going away terrified me. Winnipeg was an isolated clump of human beings protruding on the empty prairies and I could not imagine living anywhere else except in my parent's house on Machray Street. I had never been farther than Winnipeg Beach and didn't really think that life existed anywhere else.

Leaving home would be like falling off the edge of the world. No family, no friends, no food. What did people do in New York or Alberta? Especially young girls all alone. I knew some older girls who had left Winnipeg when they married but that was different because they had a husband. And there were those who were born with a talent that had to be developed, like opera singing or ballet dancing. I wouldn't be so afraid of going away if I knew that I was going to be a Risë Stevens.

But I was an incompetent. My voice was so bad that I had to mouth the words in the school choir ("Be a gold fish," Miss McCord said) in order not to put the better voices off tune.

The man I most admired in the world, my cousin Rex Winograd, sophisticated, older, who had a beautiful girlfriend, Noreen, said that it was impossible to dance with me because I didn't know how to follow.

I never let on to my father about my secret fears when I threatened to leave home. His response was scary enough. Father, a Kerenskyite, was chased out of Russia during the revolution by both the Red and Czarist armies and never spent a day out of Winnipeg since he arrived in 1917, almost 30 years before. He believed that anyone, even a man, who left Winnipeg would get beaten up or have a nervous breakdown.

"People out there are wolves. They don't care if you live or die. Who is going to cook all those good things for you or make sweet sixteen parties except your mother?"

I knew my parents loved me even though I was ungifted, plump, and talked back. After I made my bed in the morning, my mother always remade it when I was at school because I left lumps under the spread.

Mother was my comforter and protector, not to be found anywhere else but at home.

She was the only one who did not object to my restrained arrangements for a sweet sixteen. Father thought it stupid just to invite girls — but it was Cousin Rex Winograd who really pressured me.

Rex, my mother's first cousin, was well over six feet with a barrel chest and narrow hips. His legs were long and his feet shod in brown crocodile shoes. Rex's voice was unmistakeable, resonant yet sharp, crackling a bit, as if he was talking through a microphone, like a great leader announcing war. He had a Clark Gable moustache and he always looked directly into women's eyes, his forehead creasing in amusement as they became self-conscious and shy from his stare. He owned a Rolls Royce and an oil well tiepin made of diamonds.

Rex was an entrepreneur. He was not a frequent visitor to our house but when he did come mother and I stopped whatever we were doing and listened to his stories of the rich and powerful in Winnipeg and the world — and how he humbled all of them.

Father's eyes drooped as soon as Rex began his epic chants and mother had to remove the cup of tea from father's hand when he fell asleep.

Rex had so many important things to say that our

news, my sweet sixteen, hardly seemed worth mentioning. But Rex was interested. So much so he offered to have it at his house, in the aquarium conservatory, with caterers, for at least fifty young people, mixed of course.

"Just make sure the boys don't get drunk and start fooling around with my fish. Verna needs a push and a big coming out party will do the trick. The English know what to do with a girl who hides in corners. They buy her a ball gown, a tiara, and *mishkedrinen*, the same girl is transformed from a pale nobody into a debutante. A debutante is like a blue chip stock on the marriage exchange, Sydney," Rex added, poking father awake.

Rex studied the activities of the British upper classes. He claimed that his dead mother, Fiona McNabb, had left papers proving that she was a descendant of a Scotch Duke. Rex even tried to change his name from Rex Winograd to Lord Rex Winograd, but this was rejected by the registrar who called it "a frivolous application." Despite the ruling, Rex signed in at hotels as Lord Rex Winograd and had his note paper printed with a gold Lord before the Rex. He always signed his checks with the noble prefix.

Along with his usual reading matter, *The Northern Miner*, *Dog Racing*, and sunbathing magazines, Rex subscribed to *Country Life* in which he read about his relatives, the Argyles, the Ogilvies, and Lady Diana Cooper, who, he claimed, had connections with the Scotch aristocracy.

"Frankly speaking, Fanny, I have more in common with the Duke of Argyle than with you. The Duke and I have not had the pleasure of shaking hands as yet, but we both have the people looking to us to show them the way. No one has ever looked to a mere Winograd for leadership qualities."

The idea of a coming out party and being a debutante with or without a tiara made me sick.

The closest thing to a coming out party I had ever attended was at Popular Carol's house. My parents considered Popular Carol mature for her age, but in a wise, not in a dangerous, sexual, way. She went steady with a boy in third year at Harvard University and wore his fraternity pin on her cashmere sweater, just at the tip of her nipple.

All the parents spoke well of her. It wasn't only because she had the ideal boyfriend. Carol could sit with old ladies and talk to them about arthritis for hours. She would go in my mother's kitchen and compliment her on her cooking, her clothes, and then practically curtsy to my father in the living room. I always avoided encounters with other people's parents.

Popular Carol had a good figure and her voice was all trill and lilt — she laughed at everyone's jokes, even mine.

At her party she tried to make sure that everyone had a good time and when she noticed that no one asked me or the unpopular Carols to dance, she gathered boys and girls together for a singsong around the grand piano, while her elderly boyfriend played. Carol noticed my gloomy expression. "Show your dimples, Verna. Look as if you are enjoying yourself."

But the presence of boys made me anxious. I stood far away from them because I was certain they didn't like me. Carol was sorry that I was not as happy as she, but it didn't spoil her enthusiasm. And the boys responded to her gaity. She was the Queen of Optimism and I was the Princess of Paranoia. I thought I heard the boys snickering about my thick waist and suspected they kept away from me because my conversation had an edge. I was sure they knew I talked back to my father.

It was much better to spend a Saturday night alone with one of the unpopular Carols or Norma Bled. After a few probing questions and confessions we would agree that Popular Carol was gushy, even insincere. But we would never say this in a company larger than two, because we might be accused of being jealous.

Norma Bled, Norma Shneer, the unpopular Carols and myself shared one misery together at Popular Carol's sweet sixteen. Our misery was Kenny, the milkman's son.

We were in love with him although we never admitted it to each other.

I knew the others were in love because their reaction to him was the same as mine. Their eyes rested upon his face when he wasn't looking, and they turned pink if he said "hi," in the corridor at school. We would talk about every boy in Winnipeg, except Kenny. If we mentioned his name aloud some edge in our voices might reveal our secret. At the party we competed for his attention without trying to make it obvious. Kenny was agreeable but slippery. He would start talking to me about a book I had loaned him, Look Homeward Angel, and just as I thought I caught his attention a Norma would come up and he seemed only too happy to be diverted.

Kenny's brown eyes had a dreamy look that revealed a wish to escape from his father's bottles that he carried summer mornings. His shoulders were broad and he was stronger than the boys whose fathers were doctors but this was nothing to him. Kenny was interested in the mind. At the mention of Thomas à Becket, or Carlyle, or Wolfe, his impassivity left him and you could see that he hoped they might become as important in his life as butter and cream.

We were sensitive girls and wanted Kenny to know that it was his intellect that counted, not his working-class background. But he was so vulnerable that none of us dared speak of dairy products when he was standing near.

If I invited boys to my sweet sixteen, Kenny would have to be on the list. But I wanted to enjoy my party and I knew the Normas and the unpopular Carols, in their off-hand manner, which I cultivated myself, might monopolize Kenny's attention. I did not want to become obsessed with the behavior of my best friends at my most important party.

Better to think small and be content. Cousin Rex Winograd's deb party would bring misery, the betrayal of friends and my own humiliation.

Mother and father were delighted with Rex's offer. Rex, despite his flash, wasn't usually so ready to spend money on others and my father felt he should take advantage of Rex's generosity before he changed his mind.

There was someone, however, who might be able to confront disaster and smash it: Auntie Zora, father's sister who never agreed with him about anything. She was a strong, tall woman with good white teeth and a long stride. Everybody's business was her business and she could mix in where she wasn't wanted with enough zeal to collapse the opposition. Zora knew what was best for everyone, especially "the little person." She had social democratic principles and thought that no one need earn more than Gerald, her husband, a rather lazy optician. "If we can live off so much a year, so can they." It was her belief that everyone who made more money than Gerald must be brought down to his level of income. In that way "the little person" would somehow benefit. Father said, "My sister Zora is a true socialist; her politics are based on envy." Zora had found the golden mean of living standards and she just wanted those who earned more than Gerald, as well as those who earned less, to share her good fortune.

The enemy for Zora was income tax evaders. She saw one in every candy shop owner, every rag merchant, and especially "medical men," as Zora called doctors. Even Mr. Shimkin, the vegetable man who slowly made his way down Machray Street with his horse and wagon, was suspected by Zora of storing hot cash under the spinach. But there was no doubt in Zora's mind that the grand panjandrum of cheaters was Lord Rex Winograd.

"Someday," Zora warned, "a leader will take over this country who will know exactly what to do with the Rex Winograds." And she would swallow her tea in a gulp, as if toasting her prophecy.

Zora was a pioneer of consumerism — shopkeepers and restaurant owners were the enemy and she was their scourge. Mother always wanted to hide under the table when Zora opened her sandwiches at Oscar's Delicatessen to check the fat on the meat. And one rewarding afternoon Zora found a used Bandaid in her chicken salad sandwich at Porter's Druggist and had the city close the counter for a week. They knew Zora well at Eaton's complaint department — she always tried out shoes for six weeks before she brought them back because of "the poor workmanship."

Although Zora professed to despise Rex, I noticed she softened her talk in his presence. Even an amazon like Zora, who believed that everything should be even-steven between the sexes, was not to be trusted when Lord Rex Winograd smiled upon her.

But Zora would disapprove of a catered sweet six-teen party — ostentation, waste, all for the purpose of "the mating function." She described Popular Carol's party that way. "I really believe," she said, "that social functions should only have two purposes: fund raising or intellectual. If you read Browning out loud you can invite a hundred people and not feel guilty."

Zora had gone to a Russian gymnasium where she had been taught Tolstoy, Turgenev and Dostoevsky. "A line from Pushkin excites me more than a diamond bracelet."

When I went to see Zora she was sitting at her desk in her study (my mother didn't have a desk, she had her kitchen table), sealing envelopes for the CCF. She gave me some to lick while I told her my troubles. I didn't say anything about my real reasons for not wanting Rex's party — the problem with Kenny and my girlfriends and the fact that I would be creeping along the walls at my own party. Zora was too self-confident to understand.

I appealed to her high-mindedness. I told her that I'd rather Rex gave all that money to the Shriners' hospital for crippled children than spend it on me. I even told her that I intended to join a young people's socialist movement to help negroes in the southern United States.

Zora looked at me over her horn-rimmed glasses. "Look here, if you are going to sulk at your own party, St. Bernadette, don't go through with it. I'm sure that Rex will do something cheap anyway. Like bring Noreen, the torch singer. He has as much in common with the Duke of Marlborough as I have with the Princess of Pinsk."

"Not Marlborough," I said, "Argyle."

But before I could get on to the difference between Scotch and English dukes she pushed aside the envelopes and said, "Let's go see your father."

We took the streetcar and arrived at my parents' house about four o'clock and as soon as we came in mother laid the table for coffee. Zora brought up the subject while we ate chopped egg and olive sandwiches (open face, they were less fattening), melted cheese squares, three kinds of pastry, including a new recipe mother was trying out called Mrs. Sokolov's honeyed nuts.

"Why do you let Rex push you around, Sydney?"

Father was surprised.

"That sweet sixteen he wants to have for Verna. It will be out of your control, Sydney. Rex is wild. Remember his collection of loaded rifles. One of the boys will get into it after a few glasses of Rex's punch. I know his recipe: one glass pineapple juice, one cup sugar, and three glasses of rye."

Mother looked as if she had swallowed the punch bowl.

Zora, encouraged, added, "A lot of people will say that you are accepting Rex's charity, that you can't afford to throw your own." (Zora didn't like people richer than herself, but she didn't want her brother to look poor either.)

Here was a knot for my parents. Rex was certainly uncontrollable and he could get mean later, especially if he thought he had done you a favor. My parents began to worry.

Zora had done well. Father took no more interest in the coming out party (his interest in any kind of social function was never long lasting) and mother was worked up. She imagined a Cyprian debauch — drunken Normas letting the water out of Rex's aquarium and all the tropical fish going down the drain. She saw the fruit of the dwarf citrus trees in the conservatory used to smash panes of glass out of the skylight. She heard Noreen leading the boys and girls in a singsong with dirty words. And there would be an ambulance, several ambulances carrying the wounded, shot by Popular Carol's frat man who, hiccuping Crown Royal, had seized one of the loaded rifles. The phone calls from the mothers the following morning would be intolerable.

Mother had to tell Rex that she didn't want him to have a party — which meant she would have to phone him between midnight and three in the morning, the only time he was home and not sleeping. Rex was an insomniac and he air layered his plants and cooked carp soup during those hours.

I heard her whisper, so as not to wake father, as she broke the news to Rex.

"The sweet sixteen has to be at my house Rex. A mother called me, I won't say which one, and begged me to keep the affair small for her daughter's sake. The girl, one of Verna's best friends, is having nervous trouble. And she asked me not to have boys as a special favor."

Mother's white lie unwittingly described me.

Rex had almost forgotten about his offer by this time and took my mother's rejection rather well.

"Someday, Fanny, you will be sorry that you didn't let me do this for you. It would have been Verna's first chance to make something of her life and it might be her last. Don't ask me to give her a party when she's thirty and hanging around your house. She'll be like a hump on your back."

2
Kenny

The first plan, my plan for the sweet sixteen, was now back in play — no boys, lots of food and only the girls I liked.

Popular Carol was coming and didn't mind about the party being all girls because her steady had returned to Harvard University and she had promised not to date other boys. The frat man sent her a single rose every Saturday and she spent her Saturday nights with the girls, bringing the rose along and fondling it during the evening.

My sweet sixteen was really an extension of these evenings — we danced to "Blue Tango," made no-bake fudgies, and discussed whom we really hated, present company excluded. The presence of Popular Carol was flattering, an example of noblesse oblige — all the girl had to do was remove her pin and she could go out with any boy she wanted.

Mother, to make the sweet sixteen more significant than just another Saturday, planned an elaborate sit-down supper at nine o'clock and my brother promised to stay in his bedroom.

Mother began to prepare for the party well in advance. She ordered the bread two days before for the sandwich loaf because it had to be cut in long horizontal slabs by the baker's special machine. She made three different fillings: tuna fish, egg, and cucumber, and spread them over the slabs and then covered the whole with a whipped cream cheese and lemon preparation. Afterwards, she stuck tooth picks at each corner of the loaf so the waxed paper wouldn't mess up the olive pattern on the cream cheese. She put a wet, but not dripping, cloth towel over the waxed paper to keep the loaf moist until the evening. The dining room table was set with a damask cloth, tall candles and the Aynsley china. Norma Bled, Norma Shneer, the Carols and I would be able to eat as much as we wanted without hiding our appetites from boys. It was considered unseemly to eat a lot in front of the opposite sex. On the few occasions I did go out with boys, to a drive-in or a snack bar, I always, on instructions from mother, ordered clear tea with lemon.

"If a boy asks you out to eat, order the cheapest thing on the menu. And you of all people, Verna, don't need any extra calories."

The girls dressed for my party in their best tartan skirts, pleated at the back but straight in the front, held together by enlarged safety pins that were supposed to show midway on the thigh. I wore a brown jumper. Plaid skirts and sweaters eliminated whatever concavity I had between hips and breast — what other girls called their waist. The jumper, I hoped, made me look as long and lean as a Balkan Sobranie but my brother said the effect was more like that of the stub end of a cigar.

"Don't buy brown the next time," mother said.

I sat in my father's chair around which mother had wound pink ribbon and opened boxes of Yardley soap, leather autograph books and rose geranium bubble bath, while mother brought out tomato juice in crystal glasses. It was like my tenth birthday, except better because of the grownup china and food. I never felt safer or surer of everyone.

Our favorite topic was the future. We would all marry, of course, but who would be first? Popular Carol, certainly; she was practically engaged. But after marriage, who would move away from Winnipeg and cause their parents pain? The best course was to marry a Winnipeg boy who worked in his father's business in the city.

The future had little to do with my sweet sixteen, a celebration of the past, my sanctuary where all things were known and true. We were happy little girls who skipped to the dining room table when my mother called us to eat; we were going to play pass the secret with our mouths full during the meal and mother had even hidden prizes in the Russian Butter Cake.

She brought out Cream Cheese Surprise and I cut the first slice revealing gold, pink and pale green ribbons at the end of my stroke. We clapped at the intricacy of its structure and the satisfying thought that it would soon be going into our mouths.

This was the finest moment of my life. I cut gigantic portions for everyone and handed out the plates as if they were our tickets to the sweepstakes of happiness.

Then the doorbell rang through our laughter and my brother, who answered, came into the dining room and announced, smirking, "Verna, it's a boy and he wants to talk to you."

Six stomachs, mine included, sickened. I could even hear sort of a wail coming from the direction of Norma Bled's navel. The room was quiet except for the alimentary noises, and the forks, held so high in the air, came down to settle beside the plates. I left the dining room with nonchalance, trying to be as poised as Popular Carol would have been.

Standing outside on my doorstep, for the first time in his life, was Kenny the milkman's son. He was holding a book, *Look Homeward Angel*, in his hand.

"I thought I better return your book," he said, barely getting the words out.

No boy in town would ever return a book to a girl on a Saturday night unless he wanted to spend the whole evening with her. Kenny didn't know about the hungry virgins sitting in the dining room. He had chosen me, not them. He must have felt something was wrong and backed slightly into the cold night already wanting to escape. And I wanted to go with him and leave the Cream Cheese Surprise, Russian Butter Cake and all the Melting Moments behind. But I knew I had to ask him in and throw him to the girls — even Popular Carol was not to be trusted, frat pin and all. If only I had the nerve to suggest that we go for a walk (it was thirty below outside) and discuss *Look Homeward Angel* away from my house, and leave everyone else to celebrate my sweet sixteen. Instead, I asked Kenny inside and told him that it was my birthday and offered him a slice of the Surprise.

My appetite was gone but Kenny looked hungry. When he walked in everyone clapped, as they had done for the food. We sat him in my birthday chair and piled food upon his plate. Maybe a milkman's son didn't get enough to eat at home. He looked pleased and ate everything mother made, not noticing the rest of us left our plates full. Kenny, usually so withdrawn in the presence of one girl, expanded in the company of six and spoke for several minutes without stopping.

"I really admire brains," he said. "My friend, Harvey Stone, is so smart that he thinks in parallelograms, not words and pictures like everyone else. Sometimes, when Harvey sits in that funny way with his jaw sagging, I think, maybe this is it, the moment that a cure for cancer is being found."

Until Kenny enlightened us, I always thought Harvey Stone an eyesore and avoided sitting next to him at school. Norma Bled spoke for all of us when she interrupted Kenny. "I guess we all should be nicer to Harvey. I'm sure Einstein wasn't much to look at in his youth."

Kenny was at his ease, an Ottoman pasha within his seraglio, and his words were gifts, pearls, for the houris. He continued to describe his search for cultivated human beings. "I admire girls with brains too. Which of you has read Emile Zola or Joseph Conrad or T. S. Eliot?"

I tried to think of a literary reference which would tie Kenny to me forever, but Norma Bled, who also read books, was very quick. A slight girl with glasses, who looked twelve instead of sixteen because her breasts had not yet developed, Norma rarely opened her mouth when there were more than two present, especially if there was a boy in the company. But at the words T. S. Eliot, she leaned back on the chesterfield, her body undulating in a way none of us had ever seen before, and recited without hesitation:

> When lovely woman stoops to folly and
> Paces about her room again, alone,
> She smooths her hair with automatic hand
> And puts a record on the gramophone.

Such a silence in my mother's living room. Norma Bled, the darkest horse of the evening, the hundred to one shot, was way up front.

The rest were barely moving and we were thinking very hard, searching, stretching our minds for a quotation that would overtake Norma Bled's.

Popular Carol, who never read anything but *Seventeen*, was definitely handicapped.

The others, a little better off, had stopped trading Nancy Drews and could do half a lap with Daphne Du Maurier. But a line like "The first Mrs. De Winter is the true chatelaine of Manderly" would not do.

I traveled farther than them with Thomas Wolfe but could not think of an apt quotation. The only verse I knew by heart was from "The Highwayman" concerning Bess, the landlord's daughter, and I kept it to myself.

Norma's recitation had a strong effect upon Kenny. He closed his eyes and put his hands up in the air.

"Let me touch those words."

His fingers groped in the air as if to catch them and with his arms out front like a somnambulist, he went over to the chesterfield and sat beside Norma.

I tried to seduce him with, "I know what the S. stands for in T. S. Eliot," but he didn't want to hear.

Popular Carol, forgetting her rose, Harvard, frat pin, just hating to lose, even the least thing she wanted, tried to swing Kenny's attention away from Norma Bled to herself with my bubble bath, a present from one of the unpopular Carols. They, along with the other Norma, had become watchers by this time, and left Popular Carol, Norma Bled and myself to continue the contest.

Kenny had never seen bubble bath before and Popular Carol said to him, "I pour rose geranium every night in my tub." Her father, a famous man in our town, used it in "his tub too." It was just as if Margaret Truman had said that her father bubble bathed in the White House. Kenny knew how important Carol's father was and accepted the sachet she pressed on him to take home.

That's when Popular Carol saw her opportunity. She was supposed to drive the girls home in her father's Caddie and asked Kenny if he wanted a lift. We knew he would sit in front with her while she stuffed Norma Bled and the others in the back and then she would drop Kenny off last. Carol, however, thought she owed something to her hostess, and said, "Maybe you don't want to come in my car Kenny — maybe you want to stay on a bit with Verna?"

I wanted to slap her face.

Kenny never responded. The girls left and he stayed behind. The dead look in Norma Bled's eyes and Popular Carol's rigid smile, as they filed out, gave me hope that I had won. I stood very close to him and asked if he wanted to come back in the living room with me and sit. My parents and Ronnie had gone to bed. I was excited and had finally thought of three quotations by George Bernard Shaw that could keep the conversation going for another fifteen minutes.

I had triumphed on my sixteenth birthday.

But Kenny was not as animated as before and didn't say anything for a moment.

Then he asked, "Do you think Carol has really gone? Could she be waiting around the corner for me to come out?"

At first I didn't know what was on his mind, but I replied that Carol wouldn't wait because the others had to be home by midnight and it was past that now.

Kenny seemed relieved and for the first time in the evening looked me straight in the face. He said, "I have to go now. Thanks for the Melting Moments and bubble bath."

I realized then why he had stayed on. Kenny was ashamed of his house. He was afraid that Popular Carol would see it. No one knew where Kenny lived, or what his father's house looked like, and that's the way he wanted it.

3
The
Wrongies

I certainly wasn't ashamed of my house.

It was on the best end of Machray Street, only a block from the Red River, near the big oak trees on the corner. Daddy said the only reason he didn't buy a house on the river was because he was afraid that my brother and I might roll down the steep bank and drown. My parents bought the house before I was born and I lived there until I was married.

Everyone on Machray planted snapdragons, salvias and sweet peas, bright annuals that flourished in the long days of Winnipeg's brief summer — except for Ida Bled who grew poppies for the seeds to make cookies and cakes. One day the Mounties knocked on Ida's door and asked to see her poppies because they thought she was growing *Papaver somniforum*, the opium flower. Ida panicked, tore her poppies out of the ground and planted snapdragons like the rest of her neighbors, although it turned out afterwards that her poppies were not the variety dope fiends liked.

Most of the people living near us were Jewish, small businessmen and their families, except for the Mercers who lived next door — he was a Methodist small businessman. In December the Mercers' house shone in the evening blackness for a good half mile because they had the only Christmas lights on the street.

Most of our Jewish neighbors were second generation Canadians who had moved away from their parents' small wooden bungalows on the other side of Main Street, which crossed Machray less than a mile from the Red River. The river end of Machray had bigger houses and more yard space for lilac bushes, bird baths, and lythrum.

Anyone who lived on the river side of Machray sent their children to Luxton school from grade one till nine. Consequently, half of Luxton's pupils were Jewish, but from varying social backgrounds. Machray was on the top of the social heap because we had a couple of lawyers and dentists on the street. Many of the pupils at Luxton were children of workers in the needle trade; few of them wished to follow their parents' footsteps.

Miss McCord once asked us what we wished to be when we grew up and every boy in my class answered lawyer, doctor or dentist. Some of the girls said home economist or teacher, but most of us believed that the best thing to be was "good wife and mother." A shock went through the class when a girl named Ruby, who sat in the back seat in the farthest row, answered "presser."

Miss McCord didn't understand.

"What's a presser?"

"It's what my mother and father do: iron clothes at the wholesale."

Everyone in the class was embarrassed, partly because Ruby had such a low ambition, but mostly because her mother had to work.

The rest of the pupils came from middle and working-class Ukrainian families, and there were a few Anglo-Saxon kids whose parents had not yet moved to Fort Rouge, Crescentwood, or Fort Garry, anywhere away from the north end.

The teachers were mostly Scotch — names like McKay, McCord, McCloud, Duncan, and McKinley were as familiar to us, whose grandfathers or fathers came from eastern Europe, as to any child born between Dumfries and the Caledonian Canal.

The teachers dealt with the mouthy Jewish kids as best they could, realizing we hadn't been trained at home to keep quiet when another talked and to stand up when a lady walked in. There was little overt anti-Semitism — perhaps because we were in the majority.

The atmosphere only became uncomfortable during Christmas and Easter when the teachers made us read passages aloud from the New Testament about the birth of Christ and the Crucifixion. We resented especially the chapters about the Crucifixion, which put our ancestors in a bad light and caused strained theological arguments with the Ukrainian kids.

"There's the proof in the Bible. You guys killed Christ."

"Nah, it was the Romans. Even Mr. McIntyre says so," (a fair-minded teacher who always stated this view before the Crucifixion readings).

We had our revenge during the Christmas carol season when we practiced a kind of passive resistance.

Although we grudgingly sang all the carols, there was an understanding not to utter the words Christ or Savior during the carolling. Kusy Gwertzman said it was all right to sing out Jesus, but not Little Lord Jesus — his reasoning being obscure. We started off under the direction of our edgy teachers with fairly satisfactory tone and adequate diction, until we reached the key words which came often in "Adeste Fidelis" and "God Rest Ye Merry Gentlemen." There would be a hissing sound from the sudden intake of our collective breaths and Joan Karasevitch and Margaret Campbell were forced to sing an unrehearsed duet as everyone else clamped their teeth together. When the forbidden words had passed we would resume, not without some stragglers, at the next safe passage.

I don't recall a McKay or a Dunbar who had the courage for any confrontation.

Choir singing was the most important activity throughout the year. There was the girls' junior high choir, the boys' junior high choir, and the best mixed voice junior high choir. Each class was automatically formed into a choir as well, although less was expected from the sound. This meant there was no escape for the tone deaf who had to mouth their way through, "Step I with my cromach to the Isles."

The Manitoba song book had one of the most complete selections of Scotch folk airs in all the educational systems of North America. Miss McCord, Miss Dunbar, Miss McKay and Miss McKinley enthusiastically led Wanda Kunka, Hymie Birnboim, Boris Bachynski and Shulamith Gorelick from the lowland Selkirk borders to Loch Maree in the highlands with "Sing Aye for the Bonnets of Bonnie Dundee."

Neither teachers nor pupils thought the song selection in any way incongruous.

Other than differences over the interpretation of the Gospels (and the desire to suppress the New Testament entirely on the part of militants like Kusy Gwertzman) our teacher–student relationship was satisfactory. Team spirit flourished during the home and school tea. The teachers asked the mothers to bring a "small square" for the event. On the day of the tea, the teachers would be overwhelmed by eastern Europe's culinary riches. Instead of shortbreads and matrimonial cake, the pupils would carry in eight-layered tortes filled with apricots, paper-thin strudels set with turkish delight, and a hundred different kinds of cookies made with strange ingredients: poppyseeds, buckwheat, honey, and prunes.

Unconsciously, the mothers' rule of thumb was: the worse their English, the more lavish their contribution. In this way they made up for social inadequacies during their talks with Misses Dunbar, McKinley, McIver and others. My mother felt no need for self-expression at the Luxton Home and School Tea, having been a teacher herself. Her contributions were aptly named nothings.

There were parts of the north end, past the Selkirk bridge toward the city hall, where mothers didn't bake for home and school teas, where people put newspapers on their windows instead of blinds, let alone curtains, and weeds grew. This was where many of the north-end wrongies lived.

The wrongies' parents didn't speak English and were a symbol of the despised old country to their children.

The boys found their pride and living space at certain cafés and snack bars along Main Street — the This is It and the Tophs.

I used to walk by Tophs with my eyes closed so the wrongies inside wouldn't catch me peeking at the sunbathing magazines displayed in the windows. None of the Carols or Normas ever went inside. Burt the Boozer, Chicken Brassiere and Kusy Gwertzman, who hung around playing cards, would be sure to make the atmosphere uncomfortable for girls from the river side of Machray Street.

Kusy was a kid with a mean streak who would sit on the streetcar with one leg tucked under so that the old ladies standing in front of him would think he was a child amputee. When he rose on his two good legs he'd smirk at their dirty looks. Kusy, Chicken and Boozer used to make money by enticing farmers into poker games at every fleabag hotel in Manitoba. No one from Mafeking or Mud Falls were safe when that trio hit town.

Chicken's mother was responsible for his first name. Her lungs had enlarged, trying to reach her son over the years. She would stick her neck out of the window from her upstairs apartment and bellow, "*Faigeleh, Faigeleh*" (little bird, little bird), an affectionate yiddish diminutive used to lull infants to sleep.

Faigeleh was usually somewhere setting fires with his friends and didn't appreciate her old country manner of speech. The language of the street was English and none of the wrongies wanted it generally known that their parents spoke only Yiddish at home.

They even tried to encourage a little bilingualism. When Chicken's or Kusy's parents asked them, in Yiddish, where they had been for the last three days, they always replied, briefly and sullenly, in English. The most apt translation for *Faigeleh*, the wrongies thought, was Chicken.

The second part of Chicken's name was acquired in Latin class when Chicken awkwardly translated a passage from Latin into English, that read, "And the Roman soldiers carried the flaming braziers high about their heads." Hence Chicken Brassiere.

Sometimes my brother Ronnie, a typical middle-class boy, ventured into Tophs. The wrongies once examined his watch, passed it from one to another and congratulated him. "Best quality bar mitzvah type watch, boy. Leave it with us and we'll see that it gets properly cleaned." Ronny returned without the watch and my parents had nothing to say except, "We told you not to go into Tophs."

The wrongies were mostly Jewish, except for a couple of straying Ukrainians. They liked to stand in front of the north end synagogue on Yom Kippur, when the pious fasted, and munch on pork spare ribs from a greasy brown bag. They considered their ploy successful if an apoplectic beadle rushed at them close enough so they could offer him a bit.

Few of the wrongies went in for violent crimes except for the occasional conflagration.

My Great Uncle Miller lived in the wrongie section,

on Lancaster Street, and we used to visit him every Sunday because he was the patriarch of my mother's family.

I was sure Kenny lived somewhere near Lancaster and although he was not classifiable as a wrongie, he was just as ashamed of his background. I wondered whether, if I told Kenny that I had a respected relative living on these mean streets, he might have felt more at ease with me.

My father went to Lancaster reluctantly, forced by my mother and grandmother to drive them there. When Daddy entered Great Uncle Miller's house he enjoyed his visit, because he said that Great Uncle was educated (not like the rest of my mother's family) and read the editorial page. But when he left the Miller's house, a loathing for the district would come over him and he would warn me never to go there except with him in the car.

I never wandered about the wrongie section but not because of father's advice. I was afraid of bumping into Kenny and seeing his house. I told myself that I didn't care if Kenny lived in a hen coop in Chicken Brassiere's backyard. But I was born on Machray Street and had a distaste for anything less.

And Kenny certainly would have hated me and stayed away from me forever if he thought I had discovered his home.

4
Fanny
the Feeder

My father was not born in Canada and thought himself better than the earlier immigrants, who arrived in the 1880s. Great Uncle was an exception because Daddy said he had been well educated in the old country even though he hadn't done well in the new.

In the old country everyone — merchants and cart haulers — looked up to the scholar. It had been the poorest, Daddy would repeat, who emigrated first because they had the least at stake — as soon as they came to Winnipeg they found the best way to be respected was to make money, not study the Talmud.

When my father arrived he found that the people he thought scum in the old country had done better than the scholars. "Life was harder for me," he would say, "because I wasn't ready to do anything to get ahead, like slice corned beef in a delicatessen. One reason I like your Great Uncle Miller: he never stood behind a shop counter."

My father's scorn of trade, even though he came from a race of middlemen, was equal to that of an eighteenth-century Hapsburg prince. He had been educated at a gymnasium (a classical college) and his grandparents were planning to send him to Vienna to further his education when the Revolution interfered. He never explained exactly how he came to Winnipeg but he was positive it was the smartest move he made in his life.

Winnipeg had everything he wanted. No Tsarists or Bolsheviks to meddle with his personal life and a climate that was dry and cold, the best for healthy lungs and longevity.

Although he had neither English or money when he arrived in 1917, he fully intended to complete his education. He worked on farms until he earned enough money to attend the Agricultural College. While he studied for a Master's degree in cereal chemistry (having learned English), Daddy brought out his sister Zora from the old country who, to his relief, immediately married a local boy, Gerald the optician.

Daddy loved everything about Winnipeg: the flatness, the "aggie boys" at the college, and especially his new job, working for a Mr. Kingsley-Peel.

He never spoke of the old country except to mention smugly that he had forgotten all his Russian.

My mother was born not very far from Machray Street. We went to the same high school. Her history teacher became my school principal. My grandmother was widowed early and mother went to normal school, became a teacher and got a job in northern Manitoba teaching pupils who were half Scotch, half Indian, with blue eyes. Mother lived with an English couple, Captain Bell and his wife, who knew nothing of farming but used lace table cloths, much to the scorn of their neighbors, and served clotted cream and seed cakes at tea time.

Although mother had to share her bed with their baby, who wet it every night, she liked the Bells and felt sorry for them because they would have been happier back in Suffolk.

Once the Bells got over the shock of housing a real live Jew (nineteen, female and afraid of the team of horses she had to ride to school) they took to her, like everyone else in mother's life, and called her Miss Sunshine.

Mother would have stayed in Birch River, but my father wrote her to come back to Winnipeg where he had met her during the summer before. He promised to support her mother if she would quit work and become his wife.

Miss Sunshine returned to Winnipeg, married, and she and my father eventually settled on Machray Street. My father was good as his word and looked after my grandmother for years until the rest of her family were able to help out.

Mother was grateful to Daddy but she always reproached him for his lack of warmth towards her mother. "You never talk to her, Sydney." She was part of the earlier immigration, uneducated, and a woman. He saw that she had a place at his table, a nice dress, and a comfortable apartment. My grandmother was at our house almost every day but the only way I knew he was aware of her presence was when he said to mother, "Fanny, tell your mother that the fish she made yesterday tasted better than usual."

To do my father justice, this was no trivial compliment.

He believed "The better the cook the better the person," and that good cooking and moral goodness were equivalent. However, he also considered cooking to be a woman's work. He never gave any man who cooked well a gold star for moral goodness.

But a woman was not necessarily worthy just because she could boil up a bean and barley soup. The point was this, "Did she know enough to scrape the fat off the soup after it had cooled?"

I used to come downstairs for breakfast and watch, with unsettled morning digestion, mother taking the fat off yesterday's soup. Even so, at supper, my father would bang his spoon on the table and say with scarcely controlled rage, "I taste fat in the soup, Fanny." Mother would flush, jump up, grab his bowl, run upstairs and hold his soup under the flourescent light in the bathroom, eyes sweeping the surface of the soup, searching for the telltale sparkle of a fat globule.

We'd sit downstairs, not eating, not drinking, like the local population waiting to hear from the microbiologist if there was plague bacillae in the town water supply. "Nothing," she'd say, with absolute confidence. "But even if I swear on the heads of the children, Sydney, you won't be satisfied." She would go to the stove, bring the pot to boil, and give him another bowl of soup taken from the bottom of the pot, where no fat descended.

Nothing made mother happier than rushing home from a tea party to release the knob on the pressure cooker. She had her explosions, like everyone else. The contents of the beet borsht dripped from the ceiling like unspeakable remnants from a bomb blast when she was still inexperienced with the cooker, and steam from a mulligatawny stew cracked the plaster behind the stove. But she learned that if you want to make a new soup every other day in a pressure cooker, you must time your life accordingly.

Mother suffered from a recurring nightmare.

She had asked a hundred people to her house for dinner and the only thing in the refrigerator was a pint of sour cream with blue mold on top. The fridge door was open and everyone was staring at the rotting cream.

That could never have happened in real life. My brother and I used to open mother's fridge and stare as if it was the Ed Sullivan variety show. On its lower shelf, a brisket stuffed with grated potato, ready to go in the oven, Hawaiian chicken livers and green peppers (a side dish that went with the meal with the brisket) and left-overs — sweet and sour tongue and a chicken leg. Upper shelf, Dutch apple pie with a soft biscuit crust, pineapple fluden and a farfel toastie mixture for the soups. Somewhere in the middle, there was a dish my brother was fond of, Mexican macaroni. The top shelf was mostly jars — half finished dills, brought up from the basement pickle room, mason screw tops filled with avocado salad and chopped herring and soups in three colors: coral cabbage, beige bean and barley, and a sort of yallery green chicken soup without noodles (they would get too soft sitting in liquid). Scattered through the refrigerator were cantaloupe and ginger marmalade, sunshine strawberry jam and a dish of watermelon preserves, a gift from our neighbor, Ida Bled (Norma's mother). Some milk bottles were well behind. We were only four in the family but you never knew who might drop in.

The lowest rack of all always contained a platter with a warning sign stuck on with a toothpick: "Children Do Not Touch, This is Zora's Stuffed Chicken." Mother had to cook for Auntie Zora, who hated kitchen work. "I've got better things to do than bang blintzes out of a pan."

Zora accused mother of Overcook.

"Your mother circles the neighborhood on the sly with covered casserole dishes, and offers them to anyone who'll take them off her hands. She's Fanny, the Human Horn of Plenty, Fanny the Feeder."

Zora used to go on about Overcook, but she never refused a cookie from mother.

All my family had their food obsessions.

Cousin Sheldon hated to chew and lived on cherries and air until he entered grade one. He then switched to mashed potatoes and bananas. Mother developed a recipe, sort of a deep fried mashed potato ball in which she secretly inserted some ground root vegetable like turnip or parsnip, so Sheldon wouldn't get rickets.

Uncle Gerald, Zora's husband, came to our house to eat omelettes, which Zora refused to make for him. (Mother cooked for Zora every other day; the rest of the time Gerald tossed salads.) Uncle Gerald ate only omelettes made in this manner: Mother separated four eggs, beat the yolks with an egg beater until frothy (she put the whites away in a covered jar for chocolate chip meringues), and heated up a frypan with a little butter until it sizzled. Ceaselessly beating, she tossed in the foaming yolks and gently cooked them until they reached the state of sponginess Uncle Gerald desired. Then she quickly took a warm plate from the oven and flipped the omelette onto it. Uncle Gerald, already waiting at the table, checked the omelette for foreign matter then wound it all around his fork, with a practiced twist, and swallowed it. My brother and I always stood by to watch.

My mother used food as a kind of a talisman. All would be well if only a person was fed what he or she desired. She hated quarrels and confrontations; her desire to please gastronomically reflected the accomodating nature of her character.

Everyone liked her, from Miss McCord, who received a box of homemade fudge from my mother on Valentines Day, to Mr. Shimkin, the vegetable man who sampled her latest soup on our 'back stairs, tasting the final results of his produce.

She tried to avoid calamity (or what she felt to be calamity) by placating and pleasing its creators — my father and his sister Zora, who specialized in what they called "plain talk." Unfortunately, when my mother tried to mollify one, she'd infuriate the other. As a result, mother's manner was tense, like a lady on roller skates keeping a wary eye for the open manhole in the road.

Every morning for thirty years, Zora called mother and told her she was spoiling father. "And I can assure you, Fanny, he's not exactly a million-dollar duke. You could have done better."

Father used to say that Zora didn't deserve marriage. "Look at Gerald, he'd starve if we didn't feed him."

Father never prepared any of the meals but he played a manager role in the household.

"I'm a supervisor. I make sure your mother gets things done," he said easily. "Fanny, there's something wrong with the furnace; Fanny, the toilet's plugged; Fanny, call the insurance man; Fanny, the dog's made a mess on the carpet."

When Zora heard him giving orders, her mouth pursed up like a prune.

"I'd never take that from Gerald."

This was the cue for father to close his eyes and cackle.

"That's because you have a dishrag in your house on Polson Avenue, not a husband."

Mother offered the same placatory services to her children as she did to Zora and her husband. She never overtly blamed me for anything and always made freshly-squeezed orange juice for breakfast.

My life had been contentment until just before my sixteenth birthday. Choir singing, elocution lessons, visits to Great Uncle Miller on Lancaster, and staring into Mother's refrigerator had satisfied me. Then I left Luxton school, went on to St. John's Tech and met Kenny. My life became disturbed, I changed and nothing was good anymore.

5
Blythe
Llewellyn
Chaftit

Mother had done the best anyone could for a daughter; but after my sweet sixteen party and my failure with Kenny, a mood of weltschmertz pressed in upon me. I idled about in the cemetery looking at the gravestones; I never replied when my father spoke to me; and when I opened the refrigerator at 4 o'clock, as was my custom, I was bored by the brisket, revolted by the ribs, found the chocolate cake mundane and loathed all the soups. I opened the cookie tins and found them filled with tedious almond crescents and dry nothings (their true name, called so because they were made of mazola oil, eggs, sugar and little else) that stuck to the top of the mouth, if you were unwise enough to eat them without a cup of tea.

I was lovesick and jealous. Since the party, Kenny had gone with Norma Bled to a lecture given by W. H. Auden who had spent a night in Winnipeg. Popular Carol had been seen giving Kenny rides in her father's Caddie. But their friendship was platonic, she said, because of the Harvard man. She still wore her pin and fondled her Saturday rose. Kenny, a milkman's son who wasn't getting such good marks at school, despite his interest in great books, could not be considered a rival.

It was impossible to confide in mother about my feelings for Kenny. If she told father he would try to be tactful with unbearable remarks like, "I saw that Kenny yesterday. He's got a bad slouch. If I were a girl, I wouldn't waste time worrying over a boy who can't stand up straight."

I refused to eat mother's food and looked for someone to blame for my misery besides Kenny. That's when I thought of Culinary Rut. "You only think of Daddy when you cook. We can't even eat hot dogs." Father, as a young man, had worked in Burns Meat Packing plant and said ever since, "I won't repeat in mixed company what goes in those wieners."

I had to express my bitterness somehow. If I was unable to talk about my failure in love I could be nasty to my mother about the next most important thing in my life, her cooking.

The only interesting time of the week was reading *Life* magazine on Wednesday. I would beat my brother home from school in order to be the first to sink into its pages. Close-ups of dead-eyed miners' wives waiting at the pits for broken bones that used to be their husbands. And on the next page an engrossing account of the way the Compte de Paris really lives, complete with hidden camera shots of his wife at Cap Ferrat.

One week *Life* published a five-page article on how to set a duck afire in your own home, with the help of a lighting fluid called cognac. There was a technicolor picture of a golden bird, high up on a silver chafing dish, and two hands, male but manicured, doing something with a liquid that was transformed into a bonfire. Long coils of orange peel and water lilies carved, as the caption explained, from white turnips, surrounded this phoenix.

Like one of Plato's chained men living in a cave, who took shadows of artificial things for reality, I had believed that my mother's cooking was the best. But *Life* broke my bonds and dragged me up the steep way out of the cave into the sun. I realized there was an excellence above and beyond the petty world of brisket and blintzes, a light that shone clearer and brighter than anything I encountered before: Flaming Duck, "Canard à l'Orange Flambée." I was determined to descend into the cave once more and expose to my fettered folk their mistaken assumptions.

Mother was in the kitchen folding egg whites for a sponge cake and I thrust the article under her nose.

"Why don't you ever cook this way?"

Mother had never seen anyone set fire to a perfectly good duck before and she thought that it was some kind of practical joke. I explained about the brandy and she sat down and scrutinized the recipe.

My parents were not teetotallers but their enthusiasm for drinking was limited to having a bottle of Seagrams V.O. and one of South African sherry that normally would lie about the house for two or three years without being consumed. A business acquaintance would occasionally send father a basket of fruit with a bottle or two tucked in between the hothouse grapes and the woody apples. Once in a while, after a vexatious day, my father would go to the kitchen cupboard for his *ketchickle* or little glass, a miniature german beer mug which looked like part of a doll's bar equipment. He would pour half a finger into it and, standing up, drink it in a gulp. On great occasions — a birthday, an anniversary — he'd pour mother the same amount of sherry in another kitchen glass (the good crystal was for ice water) and tell her to drink.

Mother had never heard of food being drenched with alcohol. I'm not sure she had even seen a bottle of brandy before although she had read about what brandy does in *The Brothers Karamazov*. While she never let on, I think the whole flambée affair was as repugnant to her as frying beetles.

But since I had told her my life was flat, stale and unprofitable on account of her cooking, she promised me that she'd make father buy brandy at the government liquor store. The only women who went there, according to father, were unmarried and reeling at midday. "No man would have them." He never made it clear if their alcoholism was a result of their unmarried state or whether their sluttish ways had turned away possible courtiers.

Another reason why mother was intrigued was because of the chafing dish. Relatives in California were always sending us care packages — Hawaiian shirts with palm trees for father, loose fuschia-colored muu-muus for mother (to make her look younger, they wrote) and occasionally boxes of dried-out dates for my brother and me. The last package had contained a copper chafing dish, apparently an indispensable item in La Jolla, which was placed unused along with everything else, including the dates, in the linen closet.

Nothing would ever have got my mother into a muu-muu, but the La Jolla relatives had thrown down the gastronomic gauntlet with the chafing dish. She had avoided the showdown for a year but now the time had come.

Just at the point when mother was seriously thinking about making Flaming Duck, Ida Bled called with a problem. The synagogue regularly invited internationally famous intellectuals to come on Friday nights and give the congregation a piece of their minds, for a fee. Would mother ask the latest lion for dinner before the lecture? Usually mother did not entertain strangers but, with Flaming Duck for dinner, she felt there was some kind of divine coincidence in Ida Bled's request and consented.

His name was Blythe Llewellyn Chaftit (all the lecturers used treble names) and no one had ever heard of him. Ida thought he had something to do with Ayn Rand or Welsh miners. "One of the two. In New York or Cardiff he's famous, so who are we to judge?"

Mother was feeling guilty because Ida had invited her to an affair six months before and she had not paid her back. Here was a chance to discharge her debt by inviting the Bleds to an affair and, at the same time, take me away from a banal existence.

When my mother said bravely to my father, "I'm going to have an affair," she was not pleading for open marriage. She wanted him to cough up money for a party or a "function." "Your mother is the kind," my Auntie Zora often pointed out, "who takes the back seat in marriage." Certainly she disliked rousing my father's temper by any novel suggestion. On the other hand, she was incapable of entering and eating in someone's house without returning the hospitality.

When my mother announced her desire for an affair, my father always closed his eyes and wailed, "Woman's worries, woman's worries, the beetles are devouring the grain in the elevators and you want your human beetles gorging in my house?" He felt that oats, wheat and barley should be the major concern of our household and tended to belittle other interests. But his plaint in reality was that of a man who knew he was beaten. My mother's coup de grace was always the same: "But Sydney, I owe them."

The most frequently discussed sin in our house was being inhospitable.

"Clara Y. has been in the city 18 months and everyone has had her over, even Dora, who's so sick, and Clara hasn't had one person back. What does she do all alone in that house?"

Clara Y. did not entertain nor did she prepare lemon sponge cake or even mocha-no-bake squares for anyone else's function or affair. If my mother was shocked, my father took a more worldly approach.

"Fanny, that woman isn't normal; she's an easterner from Fort William and they only care about themselves."

If my mother owed an invitation longer than conscience could bear, her feeling of guilt was so strong that she would do anything to avoid meeting a creditor. Once, in bitterly cold weather, we hid behind a shop, Birt Saddlery, uneasily staring at its blinking sign, We'll Tan your Hide, while a lady in a muff and fur coat passed by. My mother's ESP, always infallible, had read the bitter words, "Fanny owes me a function," written across her heart.

Aside from the invitation list the most important aspect of a function was food. My mother and Zora were the Sherlock Holmes and Dr. Watson of Winnipeg's culinary world. My mother could go straight to a dining room and guess who had baked for the function just by looking at the food spread out on the trays; specialization got to be ridiculous. Mrs. Swartz, even though entirely capable of baking a perfect example, would never encroach on the angel cake territory of Mrs. Birnbaum; she might bake a cake in the privacy of her own home, but she would never be tactless enough to let it be seen in public. Each pie, each cake or dainty, had the same personal connotation as a private family seal in Roman times.

There was also the hidden question in every sweet and sandwich filling: homemade or catered? My mother and Zora and even Millie Moss could always tell. They'd sniff around the sweet table, rejecting suspicious overly symmetrical and grossly swollen tortes. No honest housewife could have shaped and baked them. If I snatched a catered bagel, mother or Zora would pinch my arms and hiss, "Don't waste your calories on those." I had a weight problem. "A minor one," Zora would say comfortingly, "but if you don't control yourself now, you'll be a blimp at forty."

Even though Zora had not been able to find B. L. Chaftit's name in the *Who's Who* at the Carnegie Library, she was aching to meet him.

"I suppose you're going to have a formal dinner, Fanny, and hire a waitress."

Mother had thought she'd just bring the stuff from the kitchen and have me serve the plates.

"A good hostess never rises from her table. Blythe

Llewellyn Chaftit is a distinguished man of letters, not Joe Karchoom from Saskatoon."

Zora was getting that pruney look on her face.

"The guests shouldn't start eating until the hostess picks up her fork. You don't want a man like that to think you don't know these things."

Father became testy.

"Let him think we wipe the plates off with our tongues. What do I care?"

Zora adjusted the tortoiseshell hair pins which skewered her long hair in two black buns on top of her head. She had high cheekbones and always wore her hair braided in coils, like a Russian *kulich*, or twisted egg loaf, burnt black. The skewers which held the buns fast jutted out beyond her head at a forty-five degree angle. It gave her an off-center look that cockeyed or walleyed people have. "What fish eyes," father used to say. "Someone's going to stick her in the gut the way she walks all over people." When Zora fidgeted with the hairpins it was a sign that she was nudging her brain. The brain nudging was successful. Zora had an idea.

"Let me be your waitress. That way I won't have to mix Gerald, who's such a wet blanket, with famous people. And Fanny, you won't have to move a muscle at your own dinner party.

Blythe Llewellyn Chaftit.

I imagined him to be a grownup successful Kenny who traveled around the world enlightening ignorant girls like myself on the latest in great thoughts. B. L. Chaftit lived in England and presumably hung around with true thinkers like Bertrand Russell instead of the questionable ones I knew, like Harvey Stone. Despite Kenny's belief in Harvey's genius, I could not put him in the same category as Russell or Einstein. Chaftit must know the writers Kenny admired, like T. S. Eliot. Without doubt, Chaftit had read "The Wasteland," even advised Eliot on metaphors and similes. Here was a man to take me away from Winnipeg, a weightier Kenny who was too mature to be distracted by vacuous girls like Popular Carol, or skinny ones like Norma Bled.

Blythe Llewellyn Chaftit was my chance to make something of myself. When he saw and spoke to me at the dinner he might think, "Only sixteen and she knows what the S. stands for in T. S. Eliot and eats Flaming Duck!"

If my father kept quiet and let him talk, Chaftit might even help me forget Kenny.

But Zora was a worry.

"Who's going to flame the duck," I asked, knowing her incompetence in these matters.

"Your mother. I'll set the chafing dish with the duck in it, in front of her. All she has to do is strike the match. It will give graciousness to the whole dinner. Chaftit will think you eat that way every day."

Mother started cooking for the dinner four days in advance. She always made sure that her meals would please everyone by having two main courses. If the piece de resistance was roast beef, there would be a pan of stewed chicken, because, she said, "you never know." She felt that with the duck, Spanish tongue, cut in slices, covered with tomato sauce and onions, would be a suitably exotic accompaniment. We were also to have two kinds of soup and chocolate and strawberry shortcake for dessert along with dainties.

The day of the dinner, Zora came early, in full regalia rented from Malabars' Costumes. Black dress, lace apron and cap; the white gloves were her own. She bounced in full of confidence.

"Don't worry, Fanny, as long as the others don't give me away, it will be a night to remember."

Ida and Harry Bled were to pick up B. L. Chaftit at the airport and, to add class, mother had asked Emilia Stone, Harvey's mother, considered by everyone "a lady" because she spoke in low tones and never mentioned her money.

I dressed in a way that I felt brought out my most attractive aspects and reduced the least appealing. Mother said that I had good shoulders; they were more fleshed out than on other girls. I wore a black (to make me look older) off-the-shoulder blouse with white fringes and an elastic cinch belt that squeezed in my waist at least two inches. *Seventeen* claimed that vertical stripes were a must for plumper teens so mother made me a red, black and white striped skirt with a flounce on the bottom. I didn't think Chaftit would look all the way down to my feet and wore my usual saddle shoes and socks.

Blythe Llewellyn Chaftit's appearance was not spectacular. He was small and sand-colored all over, hair, complexion, suit, and shoes. He kept fooling around with his moustache — "Like a monkey looking for a louse," father said afterwards — and hardly spoke. I realized long after that he needed a drink badly but such a thought would never occur to father. It was not his habit to serve cocktails before dinner. That entailed meaningless activity: making sure there was ice, finding glasses, measuring out the right amount of rye and even buying soda and ginger ale. If mother had wanted to organize the drinks herself, he would not have objected. But she was peeling oranges in the kitchen for Flaming Duck.

The Bleds, my brother and myself, father and Emelia Stone stood around Chaftit in the living room, wondering how to pursue the kind of sophisticated conversation that the man must be used to. I felt that a literary topic was in order and asked him if he had reread Thomas Wolfe lately. Chaftit obviously read everything and I was too worldly to insult him by assuming that he had not read Thomas Wolfe years ago.

"Thomas Wolfe is for adolescents. Hysterical adolescents."

I pursued my questioning, notwithstanding my feeling that I was the number one example of the type he just mentioned.

"You must know T. S. Eliot, Mr. Chaftit. What is he really like?"

"A foul piece of shit."

My father spoke up.

"Watch your language mister. We don't talk like that in my house."

I was embarassed for my father. Chaftit was his guest and he talked to him as if he were a delivery man.

"In what way," I asked, as lightly as possible, "is T. S. Eliot a shit?"

Emelia Stone stared at me, Ida Bled gasped, and Chaftit smiled nastily.

"If I were to tell you, little girl, your father would call the police."

Zora came in then to announce dinner and when we sat down father did his best to eradicate his rudeness.

"What do you think of Winnipeg, Professor?"

Father did not know if Chaftit had even been to university but he thought it best to flatter his guest, especially after the previous conversation. It was thirty below outside and B. L. Chaftit had been in the city about an hour. We heard from under the moustache kind of a mumbling, in which we understood the words "dark" and "cold."

"Winnipeg is the most boring city in the world," I contributed. "There's nothing of interest for a man like you, Mr. Chaftit."

Chaftit didn't answer, but my father said, "Boring, boring. That's all you ever say. If you had to go out and work for a living it wouldn't be so boring."

Zora, her eyes bulging, warning us all to keep her secret, was passing soup around.

"Chicken or bean and barley?" she hissed in our ears.

But there was a space problem. The dining room was too small for her to squeeze behind the chairs of the Bleds, who were sitting along the side of the table, and get to the end where Chaftit sat. In order for Zora to serve him, she had to retrace her steps past my mother, disappear into the kitchen, and unseen by everyone in the dining room, go out the back door that led off from the kitchen. She rushed round to the front door in the snow, with a bowl of soup in each hand and eventually reappeared, this time at Chaftit's end of the table. After serving him, she'd disappear again, running out the front door and returning to the kitchen, via the sidewalk that my brother had reluctantly shoveled a few hours before.

Zora's sudden appearance at each end of the table (as well as the endless wait for cold soup) was disturbing and inexplicable to a stranger like Chaftit, who couldn't tell how she was able to pop up at each end of the table without passing through the dining room itself. He became so fascinated with her eerie appearances that he gave up on conversation.

I was mortified. The man was used to dining in vast ancient halls where butlers passed tureens of turtle soup, and then hovered about attentively, in case a guest wanted a second helping.

I tried to take B. L. Chaftit's mind off Zora.

"Have you ever met T. S. Eliot's wife?"

Chaftit looked at me.

"Wives of famous men are never interesting."

Eagerly hoping I had started a meaningful discussion, I asked why. But he didn't answer because a current of below zero air hit the table.

Zora had found it a nuisance to open the front door in the hall each time she came in with a bowl of soup so she left it ajar, for the remainder of the meal. No one said anything, but B. L. Chaftit was shuffling his feet, as if he wanted to get the circulation back into them.

We all looked to the end of the table where mother sat. Zora brought out the chafing dish containing the duck, decorated with lots of orange peels. Some matches and the bottle of brandy, just like in *Life*, were set before mother, whose face was screwed up with tension. The time had come to flame the duck.

The duck was my last chance to impress Chaftit. Perhaps he would suddenly realize that I was a cultivated young woman amidst friends and family of obvious refinement. I whispered to him, so that no one else would hear.

"We have flambée duck every Friday. It's sort of a family tradition."

Father had a smug look on his face, like a lesser prophet when one of his forecasts of disaster was about to come true. Chaftit had his eyes closed. Mother struck a match and with a frightened gesture threw it at the duck, it sizzled, snuffed out and floated around like a little boat in the sauce. Zora, blank-faced as an adjutant corporal, watching the major misfire at a regimental shooting drill, handed mother a second match which failed. Father was looking, "I told you so." Mother repeated her action until there was a flotilla of fourteen matches floating in the orange sauce.

"You've poisoned the gravy, Fanny," father announced with satisfaction. "I knew it wouldn't work. Throw it out and bring in something decent to eat."

I protested and said I didn't care if it wasn't flaming I wanted to eat it anyhow.

"You will die of sulfur poisoning and the Professor could sue us."

Mother didn't hesitate. She told Zora to bring in the Spanish tongue.

Chaftit, at last, sat up and opened his eyes.

"Tongue," he said, "tongue. I never eat anything that had been in another's mouth."

Zora said that Blythe Llewellyn Chaftit was a real fraud.

"When I gave him his soup, he pinched my bum. Would a really famous person do a thing like that?"

Obviously, B. L. Chaftit was not goin: to be my older substitute for Kenny. Anyone who pinched Zora's bum and didn't like tongue was unsuitable even though he lectured internationally. And like the rest of the boys and men I knew, it was pretty clear that he wasn't interested in me.

I was disillusioned and feared that my love for Kenny was becoming an obsession. I knew I had to put him out of my mind with someone, anyone else. I lowered my ambitions and tested a market that was cheap enough for me.

6
Handsome Harvey

I never went out with handsome boys. Or rather handsome boys never asked me out. When I approached a boy, I made sure he was homely because I was afraid a handsome one would just walk away. And I was fairly sure that the popular girls would be generous enough to leave enough space for me to maneuver around the acned, the overweight, and the large lipped.

At one of those Friday night gatherings at the Good Earth Café, where a girl could walk in without a date and without shame, I looked for Harvey Stone who was lurking near the wall in a booth. Harvey's graduating picture in the St. John's Tech *Torch* was entitled "Most likely to succeed as Axe Murderer": unkind but he did bring to mind those homely quiet boys who live blameless lives until they hack to bits with an ice pick their parents or the girl next door. Harvey's worst defect was his face. Small head, big features — eyes, nose, mouth, all fought for prominence, but the outcome of the battle was delayed by a smidge of a moustache that Harvey had grown into the fray. Kusy Gwertzman, his sometime friend, said, "Harvey, you are overloading the system with that schmoutz, watch out or you'll blow a fuse."

No one made me feel more confident than Harvey and lately I had been seeking him out for discussions on this and that. I chatted and flirted and pointed out that we were the only people in the Good Earth Café who knew what S. stood for in T. S. Eliot. Kusy Gwertzman, who knew women, convinced Harvey that I was making a play for him. The next morning Harvey asked me out on my first date.

Until Harvey's phone call, I had not added luster to the family's name. Never had a boyfriend, and my average at school was D — "for daydreaming," as Mr. McAllister, my class teacher, said when he handed me my report card. The teachers considered me too absentminded to be trusted with responsible jobs. Once Miss McCord felt that I ought to be given a chance and I became a server at the annual school tea. I was alert that afternoon rushing about with plates of raisin bread and sponge cake. Gratefully, I offered some date squares to Miss McCord and the United Church Minister who had just finished their egg sandwiches.

That's when Miss McCord turned on me.

"Girls from good homes should know enough to take away the dirty sandwich plates before offering the dainty."

Mother expressed indifference.

"We're not the type of parents who push their children. We don't give a hoot about those things. We just don't want you to feel bad."

My father said, "She's got an inferiority complex and people smell it out. Otherwise there's nothing wrong with her."

I had this affliction like a lame foot that tripped me up every time: inferiority complex. If I tried to act blasé about some disappointment, mother comforted, "You would have succeeded, Verna, if it wasn't for your IC."

She used the initials because it was a social disease like VD. I had this IC because I didn't excel in my studies or sports and I was fatter than all my friends except Norma Shneer.

After my unexpected coup, the capture of Harvey Stone for at least one date, they were heartened; they believed my ship was at least on the horizon if not exactly in port. My family had many good things to say about Harvey and his mother. Their names became well worn in our house during the week before my date.

Mother was continually giving Emelia Stone citations for good taste because she had so much money and never showed off.

"Emelia wouldn't be caught dead wearing a dress like Ida Bled's."

Ida Bled was Emelia's dead husband's first cousin, but Ida and Emelia were as different as chalk and cheese. Ida had worn a hand woven gold mesh gown weighing thirty pounds and costing God knows what at her eldest daughter's wedding.

"Emelia can buy fifty mesh dresses that weigh a hundred pounds each and have herself dragged around by a cart of horses. But she wouldn't."

Ronnie, my brother, was not so enthusiastic, but he was willing to admit Harvey into the human race by saying, "The guys shouldn't pick on him like that."

And my father remarked at dinner, "I bet Harvey never eats anything as good as this noodle pudding in his own house. Have him over for a meal, Verna, and we'll fatten him up."

The family's comments reflected three things about Harvey that were hard to ignore. He was rich, he was not respected, and he was very thin.

Emelia Stone was supposed to have the largest private income of any woman in Winnipeg. She did not pass her investment portfolio for us to see and tell but everyone knew that Mrs. Stone spent days closeted with accountants and trust company counselors.

My father said, rather smugly now that I had a date with Harvey, "She can buy Poland with her petty cash."

Harvey was a laughing stock, not so much because of

his looks, although they added to his burden, but because he was impressionable. When Kusy Gwertzman told him that his breath stank, Harvey tried to solve the problem by talking with a hand in front of his mouth. He reduced the impact of his halitosis to some degree but most people misunderstood his motivation. When he mumbled indistinctly through a cupped hand and let his fearful eyes roam back and forth in search of Kusy, who might be in a corner doing a mock faint from the stench, Harvey appeared furtive. A furtive mumbler creates suspicion and many believed that Harvey was talking about them behind his hand.

Harvey's waist was about the size of my arm. When he was born, he weighed only five pounds and was allergic to milk, eggs, and meat, except the white meat of chicken. Although he gained some weight in the ensuing years, it was not a significant amount. Yet when he rang my front door that cold Saturday night, Harvey might have been Aly Khan improved by some of Albert Schweitzer's humanitarian genes. I ran upstairs to linger over my toilette even though I had just put on galoshes. Father stopped his pacing — he had been worried about the possibility of a no-show from Harvey. Mother walked slowly to the door to greet Harvey with a casual "Good evening, Mr. Stone. I imagine you are here to pick up Verna."

Ronnie sauntered out of the kitchen on cue and nodded to Harvey just as if he were a normal person and came upstairs to warn me to stay put five minutes so I wouldn't look eager. Ronnie was my advisor on the new social whirl I was entering.

"Don't let Harvey twang your bra strap when dancing. Don't neck until the seventh date."

Harvey's dress did nothing to alleviate his physical disadvantages. The temperature in Winnipeg goes to forty below but healthy males between ten and sixty years do not walk about with scarves around their heads and ear muffs perched on top of the scarf. Nevertheless, this was what Harvey wore when my mother greeted him. He was not unconscious of his appearance. "I wear this because my ears froze last year and I had to stay away from school for a month. They had to put on compresses."

It occurred to mother that Harvey had an IC worse than mine. With correct handling, Harvey might become my steady boyfriend. She turned to father who was recovering, with a certain amount of squinting, from his first close look at Harvey.

"Get out of your chair and let Harvey sit there. I'm going to turn up the thermostat."

These were brave words.

The thermostat was sacred to my father. No one else in the family was allowed to come within a magic semi-circle he had designated around it, starting from the marble birdbath on the west end of the living room to the bookcase with *Peace of Mind*, by Joshua Loth Leibman, on the east end. Father was always suspicious, especially on cold days, that we had disobeyed him. He would stand by the thermostat for a long time muttering, "Who's been monkeying around?" Much later, after Harvey had taken me out many times and father felt our romance was in the bag, he told me how he felt the first time he saw Harvey standing in our doorway. "I thought he was going to murder your mother." But he overcame any fear he had for his wife's safety and just sat and stared. He only moved out of his chair at her command and wordlessly watched her shoot up the heat by ten degrees.

My mother knew what she was doing. By the time I came down, Harvey was so relaxed that his hand was far away from his mouth and his fingers were picking idly at the mohair blanket mother had thrown over him.

The only mishap, while I was waiting upstairs, was the fault of father. After his dislocation, he wandered into the kitchen and brought back a bowl of fruit and set it in front of the guest. Harvey started to hiss and wheeze and shake like a rusty Model T with a train whistle attached. "Nuts, nuts," he choked out incomprehensibly to my parents. At first they thought his words were simply an expression of despair at the inconvenience of his attack.

In between his spraying and shuddering, the word "allergic" was discernable. His arms flapped in the direction of the fruit bowl. Mother, panicky, rummaged through the oranges and bananas until she found a single hazelnut, still in its shell, buried at the bottom. She threw it from her, overhand, like a left fielder on a farm team. It went wide and cracked the front hall mirror. "Bad luck, Fanny," my father yelled, "bad luck for seven years." Harvey, gradually winding down, sighed, "Seven years! I've had bad luck from nuts all my life. Last summer my aunt in Louisiana mailed a sack of pecans to our door. I began to hyperventilate and the postman had to put a paper bag over my face. I was losing all my carbon dioxide."

Mother carefully removed the nut, now underneath the hall table and threw it in the cellar, via the laundry chute.

Harvey and I dated for the next ten months. It was not a passionate affair. The only time he kissed me was midnight New Year's Eve, 1952, at the Royal Alexandra Hotel dinner dance. I never had to worry about bra-snapping let alone the necking that my brother had spoken of. Harvey obviously had never heard of such things. But I was the envy of every girl in the Gold Room at the New Year's dance, because Harvey had bought me an orchid instead of the usual sweetheart rosebud corsage.

Harvey became fond of my parents and loved coming to the house. I had what he called a "physics block" and he volunteered to coach me in the subject every Monday and Thursday evenings. He convinced me that my lack of understanding in elementary physics was due to fear rather than stupidity. "A science teacher, long ago, must have humiliated you in class. Your inability to understand the simplest theorum (Harvey was brilliant in physics) is because of repressed hostility towards this teacher."

His analysis was comforting. If Harvey was correct, I could not be held responsible for bad marks. They resulted from an interesting neurosis rather than my mental laziness. The fact that I did not remember any science teacher ever making fun of me only proved to Harvey that my problem was deeply rooted. "You have suppressed the event so thoroughly even your id refuses to cope with it."

My parents were delighted that Harvey was coaching me and in gratitude mother developed a whole new set of recipes that Harvey's system could handle. As soon as we disappeared in the sun room for another go at removing my physics block, the mixmaster would begin to whine and we knew mother was making a batch of no-egg bran muffins or mashed aubergine salad, and postum. Coffee and tea gave Harvey hives. Afterwards, around 9:30 in the evening, my parents, Ronnie, Harvey and I sat around the dining room table and ate a second supper. My mother made a pot of tea especially for my father, because he claimed postum gave *him* hives.

This was the hour when Auntie Zora liked to drop in and discuss her favorite subject — income tax evaders.

"Mendel Glow, the caterer, just bought himself an Oldsmobile. I'd love to see his books. I bet he doesn't even send a tax form into the government."

Harvey's presence always made this discussion more piquant because his mother was so rich. Zora's social democratic principles made her sure that a woman with an income like Emelia Stone must be cheating the government.

"I suppose your mother is going around the world this year, for her vacation," Zora remarked lightly, her eyes darting knowingly in our direction. I imagined Mrs. Stone taking out gold bricks from a secret hiding place in the freezer behind the labeled fruit pies and, with a wink, handing them under the counter to Millie Moss, the travel agent.

Harvey was amused by Zora. Strong-minded women over thirty-five were his forte; it was people his own age who intimidated him, like Kusy Gwertzman and possibly me. He once said: "Zora, if I knew what you know about cheaters, I'd notify the tax department — a good citizen should."

Zora was intrigued by this idea of civic duty.

But father was annoyed. If you asked him what party he voted for he would refuse to answer.

"That's my business. If the wrong man got in it would be terrible for me if he found out that I voted against him. That's why we have a secret ballot."

He told Zora to mind her own business.

"You never know what you're talking about. When you deal with the government, you have to name names, give facts, write down figures. You have to be competent. All you know is gossip. So keep quiet."

Relieved of her responsibility by my father's reasoning, she thought no further about Harvey's suggestion and scooped up the rest of the eggplant on her muffin.

Manitoba High Schools at that time had a rule that if you earned a mark of seventy in all subjects during the Easter examinations, you were exempt from writing again in June. There was one catch — tests were given in June to make sure the students hadn't let their work slide. If you failed a June test all exemptions were canceled.

I received a mark of seventy on my physics examination, thanks to Harvey's coaching and insistence that I memorize the whole physics text up to and including our April work. The rest of my marks, for the first time in high school, were within the exemption range. I spent that warm spring gossiping on the school grounds, skipping boring classes, or daydreaming through the physics gibberish that Mr. McAllister subjected us to in class.

On June 8, two days before school ending for the exempt, Mr. McAllister announced that he was giving a physics test the following morning. Those who failed would have their exemptions in all other subjects as well as physics canceled. I knew that I could not pass the test. When I opened my physics text that evening it might as well have been written in ancient Norse, including the part I had already studied.

The next morning, Mr. McAllister passed out the foolscap and wrote the questions on the blackboard. The class read them and scratched away, except for me. I slid out of my desk to the floor in a graceful deliberate faint. Mr. McAllister liked girls and made allowance for their deficiencies in his subject. He was frightened and sent me to the nurses' room. I lay on the leather couch hoping that he'd forgotten about me. But after the period was over he came to the nurses' room and told me to go home. "Don't worry, Verna, I'll let you write the test tomorrow, by yourself in the Torch Room. You get some rest today." The Torch Room was a cubicle set aside for the staff of the school yearbook, now unused, because the Torch had already been distributed.

When I called Harvey after school, I was hysterical. I didn't dare tell my mother; she would have said I deserved what I got. But Harvey had read Freud and Jung and understood. He even said that Mr. McAllister was the repressive father figure who had caused my hostility to physics and should be held responsible for my mental condition. "Instead of creating a love for the subject in you, he simply aggravates your block."

We devised a simple plan. Harvey would ask to leave the class, go upstairs to the Torch Room and give me the answers.

All took place as planned. Mr. McAllister led me into the empty Torch Room, placed the written questions in front of me and left. I stared at the mumbo-jumbo for about five minutes until Harvey entered the room. He read the questions and immediately started dictating the answers to me. The process took longer than we had planned because I was dense about setting up the theorems. The door opened and Mr. McAllister walked in.

Mr. McAllister hated Harvey. Harvey never received less than a hundred in math and physics and often corrected Mr. McAllister in class, in front of everyone. If Harvey had been less of a smart alec, or better looking, I don't think Mr. McAllister would have reacted so harshly. It's demeaning to have a "horrible ugly," as Kusy called Harvey, tell you that you're wrong.

"Get out Stone. That girl isn't as stupid as you think. She can write that test as well as you. And she never gives me any back talk. You want to give her answers. I'll give you answers. I'm taking your exemptions away in all your subjects for harrassing a good student. She received a seventy in the last exam."

Mr. McAllister sent me back to class.

"We won't bother about the test, Verna, you would have done all right if it hadn't been for him."

Harvey had to write all his examinations, although he was an A plus student. I was exempt. Two days later, when the examinations started for the damned, my parents, who knew nothing of the scene in the *Torch Room*, took me on a car trip to Detroit Lakes because I had done so well that year, socially and scholastically.

When I returned two weeks later, Harvey had gone away with his mother to San Francisco. Zora said, "I'm sure it's the jumping off point for an around-the-world tour." His June marks must have been good because he was accepted at the Massachusetts Institute of Technology and Emelia said that he would never come back to Winnipeg. She didn't explain why, but I knew that I had betrayed Harvey. He wanted to spare me the shame I would feel if I had to see his face again.

7
Green Butter
and Gothic

During my association with Harvey, I used to hope that Kenny might notice that the man he most admired in the city had picked me as his Saturday night companion. I even asked Harvey if we could double-date with Kenny occasionally. I thought that Kenny might be impressed with my gentleness with Harvey, my comprehension of his asthma and sundry allergies and forget about other girls. But the only couple Harvey brought along was Kusy Gwertzman and a woman of twenty with whom he necked in the back seat of Harvey's car while we attended a Paul Robeson concert.

Once Harvey and I went to see *Madonna of the Seven Moons*, with Stewart Grainger and Phyllis Calvert. Harvey told me that the movie was Freudian symbolic. Phyllis Calvert played an Italian marchesa, a mother and hostess who had her own private priest staying in the palazzo. But six months of the year she went into a trance and ran off to Naples to be a prostitute and live with the king of the gypsies, Stewart Grainger.

Harvey and I both agreed that the only other person in Winnipeg who could participate seriously in an analysis of the movie was Kenny. No matter how much I suggested that we get together with Kenny, Harvey was indifferent to the idea of encouraging the friendship of his only fan. He shrugged his narrow shoulders and said that Kenny had problems. I assumed he meant Kenny's poor marks and his father wanting him to carry the bottles. It was callous of Harvey Stone, only son of a rich widow, to reject Kenny the milkman's son, who went around saying that Harvey was the hope of mankind.

Just before the physics test debacle, Kusy, Harvey and I, along with all the Carols and Normas, discussed the idea of spending ten days towards the end of the summer with Rabbi Ripp and his cultural youth group. The youth group, high minded young people like ourselves, were going to meet at a campsite to decide about world and personal problems and hear talks from adults with university degrees.

Rabbi Ripp was our first taste of the hip clergymen that were to proliferate in the sixties, whatever the religion. The Rabbis in the north end of Winnipeg were bearded, worried about kosher and believed that anyone under twenty-one deserved nothing but a sharrup if he spoke out of turn. There was a beardless rabbi in the south end who used to hurry up the religious services in order to get to the Blue Bomber football games. But his feeling of the contemporary went only so far as chalk talks with the boys.

Rabbi Ripp was clean shaven, in his early thirties, wore tight blue jeans, and lived in a messy old house between the south end and north end of the city. His wife let her dishes pile in the sink, left diapers on the living room floor and encouraged the Rabbi's young acolytes to visit while she nursed her baby. Rabbi Ripp conducted discussions at the university about the interpretation of dreams. He would say to all of us, sitting around the big table, "Anybody who is having a recurring dream should come and see me privately. That person is in serious trouble."

Rabbi Ripp was the most exciting thing that had happened to us for a long time. Even more exciting for me was the fact that his special confidant and chief organizer for the youth discussion group and campsite finder was Kenny. By the time August had come around, Harvey had gone to MIT and I had been the first to reserve the lower bunk, right side, by the door, in the girls' cabin at the camp near Winnipeg Beach.

The campsite wasn't even near the lake. It was a flat, treeless piece of ground corralled by a wire fence on all sides. The wooden huts stood in a semi-circle around the larger meeting and eating hall. The designer of the camp was obviously heavily influenced by the movie set of a prison camp. If there ever had been a drawing of his plan of the camp he might well have put in helmeted soldiers poised in goose-step just as other architects sketch in Lombardy poplars and dwarf conifers.

But we didn't mind because we were intellectuals and intellectuals don't care for swimming, or overnight trips with canoes on their heads, and we thought that sailing was for the international set. Somebody put up a volleyball net and there was a warped ping pong table inside the meeting hall which no one used except the oldest of the Ripp children who was nine and adopted. We knew he was adopted because he was Japanese.

Mostly we played Monopoly. The sharks, like Kusy Gwertzman, played for real money as soon as they rose at noon.

I realized the first day at camp what gall I must have had to accuse mother of being in a culinary rut. The carte du jour at camp was corn syrup and sliced bread for breakfast, with half of an apple every other day, a glutinous macaroni at lunch and a brown lumpy potage and mashed potatoes for dinner.

"Have a turd," Kusy would say, passing the pot of stew.

Kusy entertained us at table with his glimpses of the chef. The first time he spied on her she was churning potatoes in a large vat, her hair hanging loose and free.

"Unusual flavoring for mashed potatoes; instead of salt and pepper, dandruff."

Kusy also claimed that there was a large half-empty can of Beehive Corn Syrup beside the mashed potato vat in which the chef used to relieve herself.

"It's too much trouble to go all across the compound to the weehoosie, just to pee. I don't blame her."

I refused to eat during the ten days at camp. Kusy's stories about the cook would have been enough but in addition I was still lovesick. It was difficult to hold Kenny's attention more than two minutes at a time before he drifted off to mimeograph notices about our evening discussions. Although I helped him crank the machine and told him that his new idol (now that Harvey had left town), Rabbi Ripp, was truly a holy man, Kenny didn't give me any sustenance except a few kind words about my recurring dream.

He disdained Monopoly and worked with Rabbi Ripp during the day deciding on the meaningful topics for discussion that evening.

"Were Cohn and Schine anally regressive?"

"The H bomb, Henry Luce and Clare. Would he or she press the button?"

"Should a rabbi take a tip from Bishop Fulton J. Sheen?"

Kenny pushed benches around the stage in the meeting hall after evening slops and rang a cow bell to gather us together. Norma Bled, always romantic, suggested sitting around a campfire instead. But no one knew how to build one except Kusy Gwertzman who, it was whispered, burned down his father's warehouse for the insurance money. It was felt that Kusy was handier with rags soaked in gasoline than the birch bark twigs and kindling appropriate to our surroundings.

Everyone from my sweet sixteen, including Popular Carol, had come to the camp. We girls were primarily concerned with the events when the evening talks were over and the girls returned to the cabin to go to bed. We were entering university and some of the boys at the camp were already in fourth year. (Popular Carol's frat man had graduated from Harvard and they had progressed from being pinned to being engaged.) When we had undressed and tucked ourselves under the covers, the boys came over to sit or lie on our bunks on top of the blankets while we lay underneath wearing sweaters over our pyjamas. It wasn't cold outside but we thought we'd get a reputation if we allowed boys to see us in our nightwear. It was considered acceptable, however, for steady couples, like Popular Carol and Harvard, and a few others, to lie together under the blankets.

But the path was uncertain for girls like myself who had no steady boyfriend but wanted to be friendly and encourage possible suitors. The boys thought us immature if we didn't neck with our partner above the blankets; but if we allowed necking under the blankets there was a real danger from loose talk if not escaping sperm. A few girls that summer let a casual bunk date come under the blankets and Kusy Gwertzman spread the word later on in the city that they let themselves go rank. The girls had a difficult time at university the following year because of their reputations as hotpants.

The girls were outnumbered two to one at camp. In my cabin, there was a boy for every girl except Norma Shneer, who weighed 200 pounds and said she would push off any boy who climbed to her upper bunk. The worst thing that could happen was having the wrong boy on your bunk. Although a girl wasn't supposed to be too forward with a casual bunk date, it was considered mandatory to exchange a few kisses with even the most repulsive. If you refused to kiss him, the rest of the boys would boycott your bunk, because you hurt their pal's feelings.

But if you allowed too many kisses with the repulsive

one, he would come back to your bunk the next night for more. It was difficult to maintain the correct measure of diluted affection with a boy you didn't want.

Norma Shneer played the role of camp confidante and pander, matching the right girl with the right boy, using Kusy as her informer. The price we'd have to pay was letting her watch and comment on our activities from her top bunk, knowing that she would report any unusually passionate couple to Kusy, who would be playing Monopoly with the chef in the assembly room.

With Norma Shneer acting in the roles of KGB agent and grandmother there was no question of the girls losing their virginity. But even if she hadn't been present as a voyeur, the code of behavior at the camp kept us well on the right side of the blankets.

As we understood the code, we could neck, from the shoulders up, with a two-nighter casual, as long as the blankets were between us. An especially long embrace might bring forth a wolf whistle from Norma but if we came up for air our reputations wouldn't suffer. Inevitably, a boy would try to put his hand under the blankets inside our upper thigh or even squeeze a breast or two. This was called WHT (wandering hand trouble) and the girls knew that that hand expected to be rejected. After it was firmly replaced the boy would whisper with obvious relief.

"I knew you wouldn't. I should have never tried that with a nice girl like you."

We were marriage material and the boys who looked upon us as their future wives wanted fresh goods.

But if Kenny had sat on my bunk just once I would not have minded being damaged. I would have dragged him underneath the blanket while Norma Shneer took notes for Kusy and labelled me hotpants forever. Reputation, nice girl, marriage — the most important words in my life — would have become meaningless if Kenny had only made a pass. But I remained what I was because the only time Kenny came into the cabin he sat on Norma Bled's bunk. They spent the whole time underlining the important passages in *The Interpretation of Dreams* for Rabbi Ripp, lighting their work with a flashlight while I exchanged tepid kisses with a boy whose name I can't remember. I kept looking over his shoulder to make sure that Norma and Kenny didn't switch off their light.

Before camp was over Rabbi Ripp took me aside and questioned me about my personality change.

Personality change was one of those words and phrases used by Rabbi Ripp which distinguished him from everyone I had known before. I wasn't crabby (my parents' terminology). Something much deeper was occurring to my being (another of Ripp's words). The Rabbi said I had become less keen about probing the anal eroticism of capitalistic society over the last few days and that I was not eating the mashed potatoes. He thought I was suffering from manifest anxiety and was worried about my physical as well as mental being. Before I came to camp I had hinted to the Rabbi that I was having a recurring dream, knowing that his interest in me would be heightened by such news, and that he would tell Kenny, his Freudian apprentice. But I would sooner have swallowed the contents of the chef's Beehive can in the larder than reveal to them what I dreamt.

My dream was without mystery, only crass wish fulfilment that would have made Rabbi Ripp's nine year old smile. I was dressed in a wedding gown carrying a bouquet of sweet peas picked from my Great Uncle Miller's backyard (definitely a symbol of family approbation), and all the Carols and Normas were pelting Melting Moments at me, weapons without substance, full of air and sweetness that could never hurt. I had just married Kenny, who was the shadow by my side.

Rabbi Ripp questioned me about my recurring dream but I was too smart to tell him anything except that I was having one. Finally, in a pique, he told me that he was unable to let me stay out my time at camp because I wasn't participating sufficiently in the discussions and I had stopped eating. But he was kind enough to invite me to a camp reunion party that he was giving just before the university term began.

I was not unhappy about leaving camp early. I had necked with more than enough of the uglier boys and Kenny's presence prevented me from thinking there was anybody worth having except him. And my obsession was making me devious. I had stolen Norma Bled's notes on the Kinsey report which she had been preparing for her big speech the final evening at camp. It would have been too much for me to cope with if Norma's perceptions impressed Kenny enough to let her enter his private club with Rabbi Ripp.

When I arrived home, my mother said nothing except that I had lost some weight and looked better. She struggled between her desire to make me happy by cooking me all the good things I missed at camp and her realization that I would put back my pounds if she did. Mother could not stop her overcook pattern. Her nature and daily routine were set; she was too old for a personality change. But she decided that I wasn't supposed to eat what she cooked and hid away the chocolate cakes in hat boxes and encouraged Zora to take the noodle and cabbage casserole away with her on the streetcar. Every time I helped myself to extra stuffing at dinner, mother would shake her head and say it would be too bad if I put on weight before the party. Ordinarily I would have sneaked in the kitchen afterwards and vacuumed down the leftovers but heartache slowed up my appetite.

It was autumn and I bought a wide wool skirt that was a size smaller than I wore the year before. I wore the skirt, wedgie shoes and a sweater with an angora collar to Rabbi Ripp's party.

Norma Bled told me that I never looked better as we walked to the Ripp's house, both of us anticipating our first sighting of Kenny in several weeks. Norma said she had not given her lecture on the Kinsey report because she had lost her notes. Rabbi Ripp explained that she was accident prone and was deformed by a failure mechanism deep within her id. It was the id that had made Norma deliberately but unconsciously throw away her own notes.

"Rabbi Ripp said that I really want these terrible things to happen to me. Even if I get cancer, it's probably my fault."

As soon as we arrived we went from room to room looking for Kenny, although neither of us would admit it to each other. Everyone was there, Kusy, the Carols, Norma Shneer and a few of Rabbi Ripp's older friends who were in their mid-twenties. Popular Carol had organized folk dancing and everybody was clapping and stomping except Rabbi Ripp, who was sitting at a small table by the wall, out of reach of the longest flailing leg, playing chess.

His partner was a strangely dressed older man, wearing a mustard colored suit of heavyweight tweed, a tie wider and longer than those worn in Winnipeg, and brown suede shoes with buckles, which, until that moment, I had only seen on elderly ladies with orthopedic difficulties.

"Oh my God," Norma Bled squealed, her attention diverted from the quest for Kenny, "there's the Oxford don."

Norma seemed excited by this person. "I guess that's what they wear, funny thick suits. Evelyn Waugh says they put their handkerchiefs up their sleeves." Norma remembered everything she read.

"What's a don?" I asked.

"They teach at Oxford University in England. No one uses the word professor at Oxford. It's called don."

I had heard of Mafia dons and even Don Quixote, but this was the first I heard of Oxford dons.

I was always drawn towards men who lived in what I

believed to be the fine high world of ideas — Rabbi Ripp, Blythe Llewellyn Chaftit, even Harvey who thought in parallelograms, and, of course, elusive dreamy Kenny, the only good looker in the bunch. And now here in this homely basement, the Ripp's knotty pine recreation room, was a man at the peak of the intellectual world, teaching at the same university as Occam, who invented a special kind of razor eight hundred years before. Rabbi Ripp, who Kenny thought a scholar and a poet, had only a piddling job as a lecturer at the University of Manitoba.

The don person's mustard colored suit was a little worrying, however. B. L. Chaftit, a proven intellectual fraud, had worn one of a similar cut and weight. But then Chaftit, as my father later discovered, was a graduate of the University of Southhampton, barely ten years old, while this man was stamped with Oxford's ancient hallmark. Chaftit and even Rabbi Ripp were merely silver-plated.

Norma continued to inform.

"He's Martin Manheim, you must have heard of his mother. She lives in a beautiful house in the south end filled with antique furniture and is president of lots of charities. Rabbi Ripp and the rest of those guys call him M. M. He's supposed to be unbelievably intelligent and they even published an article he wrote on the editorial page of the *Free Press* last week." Norma read editorial pages.

M. M. was the most fascinating man to come my way so far, barring Kenny. Chaftit, Harvey, and even Ripp were obviously stepping stones to the don. The man had traveled all over the western world, had even spent time at Harvard (so much for Popular Carol), and lived among the great minds.

I had to make him notice me. Ordinarily I would never have dared approach someone like M. M. after my scalding Chaftit experience but I felt that I had nothing to lose, even if M. M. made fun of me. It would matter little because I was in shreds over Kenny.

I wondered what dons talked about. Norma Bled, who played chess, had already slipped over to the table as a kibitzer and murmured approval while M. M. moved his pawns. Harvey had tried to teach me chess but I apparently had carried my physics block with me to the chess board and could not tell a knight from a bishop. But I was my mother's daughter and instinctively felt that food would show me the way. I ran to Mrs. Ripp's kitchen where she was scooping out ice cream, grabbed two plates and offered them to the chess players. Rabbi Ripp looked up and smiled as Gandhi might have done when offered a bowl of bean curd after a thirty day fast.

"Verna, I knew that it would be you who would bring us nutriment while the others dance."

Norma Bled, who was never hungry and assumed others showed the same lack of appetite, realized she had been upstaged.

M. M. pushed back his chair and spoke.

"What is the flavor?"

I shyly whispered, not looking up, "Maple Walnut."

M. M. said, "I love maple walnut."

When B. L. Chaftit the fraud had been offered duck flambée and Spanish tongue, he had only sneered. But this famous Oxford man, the authentic goods, was not only gracious, but found a space for chocolate, vanilla, and maple walnut in that big dome head. This was the difference between genius and talent. Geniuses were men of simplicity who could enjoy the same things as children and dogs without condescending.

I boldly asked M. M. if he ate maple walnut ice cream at Oxford.

"No," he said quickly, "I eat green butter."

A mystifying response which made Rabbi Ripp nervous. He said, "Let's finish the game, M. M."

But the don replied, "Chess is a game for pedants. It's only the chess men themselves that are of interest."

I thought that he was uttering some kind of Sufic philosophy and kept my mouth shut.

But M. M. rose, turned to me and said, "Well, my plump little duck, let's go upstairs where it's quiet so I can learn all about you."

Norma Bled's jaw hung loose (she knew all about me) and Rabbi Ripp flushed. I followed M. M. upstairs, carrying his maple walnut ice cream.

As we sat by ourselves in Rabbi Ripp's den, I was overwhelmed by Martin Manheim's exoticism — the yellowish tinge and heavy texture of his suit, and the way he crossed his legs, a l'anglaise, letting the outer leg dangle from the knee. His quick dismissal of whom and what I believed important — Rabbi Ripp and playing chess — put him beyond my terms of reference. There was some ground to cover between this Lord Peter Wimsey darkened by a brushstroke of Spinoza, and Verna, the teenage plumpling, who had not yet figured how to attract a milkman's intellectual son depressed by the Ds on his examination papers.

I didn't want M. M. to notice any gap so I lunged forth with a Ripp-Kenny question, the kind we asked at the youth discussions. Other girls would have kept quiet and let events unfold without chatter, but this was never my way.

"Mr. Manheim," (out of respect, I always called men who looked over 25 "mister"), "when you said I eat green butter, what was your metaphorical intention behind that statement."

M. M. stared.

"I meant that I eat green butter, nothing more. Green butter is served as a savory at High Table in our College. In England, especially at Oxford, where one drinks port, a special course, the savory, is served after what you and other North Americans would call dessert. It's a peculiar custom, I admit, but the English don't like to have too sweet a taste in their mouth before port. The savory removes any aftertaste of custard. Sometimes the savory is fried oysters and bacon, occasionally sardines on toast. I think the best savory of all is green butter. Unfortunately, I don't know how the chef makes the butter green, otherwise I could give you the recipe."

I was disconcerted. He sounded more like my Aunt Zora describing the interesting smorgasbord at her Icelandic neighbors' than one who lived a life of pure thought.

I set aside this aberration and tried him out on chess. Rabbi Ripp and Kenny told me that only the finest brains could play a decent game of chess. I couldn't understand why M. M. who had a fine brain, said the pieces were more important than the game. "Surely this was a metaphor of some sort."

M. M. sighed.

"Little duck, you like to complicate things. All I meant was that I find playing chess a mathematical dead end, a bore. The sets and pieces, however, can be very beautiful. Not Ripp's, obviously, which are plastic, but people do collect chess sets because they are finely carved. I have several ivory sets which were carved in India and China centuries ago. These sets were made as objets d'art and are not considered playing sets. Doesn't your mother collect china or silver? It's the same kind of thing."

I never before had met a man who collected things just to look at. Of course, many of my mother's friends had pretty cups and saucers in their cupboards. Ida Bled collected blue china horses, but their antiquity or quality were not important. As long as the china was shaped like a horse and painted blue, Ida bought it. Cousin Rex Winograd often had pieces of jade and oriental carpets in his house, which he bought, he said, from starving Asians. His motives were commercial not aesthetic; once he bought three oriental rugs and traded them a week later for a speed boat.

The gap between myself and M. M. was widening. He talked about the importance of beauty in my life and said that I would find Oxford fascinating because of the variety and style of the buildings, from Romanesque to Ruskin neo-Gothic. I had no idea what he meant. I lived in a city where very old buildings were usually not more than fifty years old and father said they ought to be torn down because no one could afford to keep them clean anymore.

As M. M. went on about vaulted doorways and the significance of arches and apses my attention strayed, and when he said that beauty was the ultimate experience in life I began to think that he was affected, maybe even another Chaftit. However, M. M. was certainly the catch of the evening and I was well aware that all my friends, plus Rabbi Ripp, envied me for having the don's exclusive attention. I tried to pay attention to his words, but it was late and I couldn't concentrate.

When I said it was time I went home, M. M. drove me to my door. I knew I should have called my mother because I was out much later than usual. However, to show such a lack of sophistication in front of M. M. would have taken more courage than I had. I was unnerved by having an older man as an escort and worried what my mother would say. When I came in she was waiting for me and I told her that Martin Manheim had taken me home.

"It's just as if Mr. McAllister, my high school teacher, or Rabbi Ripp drove me. He's not a real date."

"Why not?" she replied. "Maybe he'll ask you out again. He comes from a very nice family."

I was surprised. I had not thought of M. M. as a Winnipeg boy. In any case, he was leaving for Oxford the following day and all he promised was a picture postcard, so I could see what a Gothic arch looked like.

Norma Bled called me the next morning to find out

about M. M. Despite my triumph, her voice was carefree and her tone was casual.

"You know Kenny came in when you and the don were upstairs. He wondered where you were. When I told him that M. M. had made a play for you, Kenny said that all the really smart guys went after Verna — first Harvey Stone, now Martin Manheim. I guess Kenny thinks there's no chance for him, you're so used to genius. We went out for coffee afterwards. Kenny told me he really admires M. M. and thinks he's smarter than Ripp. He wanted you and Manheim to come with us but he was afraid that Manheim would find him boring."

The irony.

I used to feel sorry for myself because Kenny and Rabbi Ripp sometimes referred to my "crude schoolgirl attitudes" — before M. M. Now I had suddenly become a frightening female intellectual. I was a Rebecca West or Virginia Woolf and priced myself out of the market. I didn't feel smarter after one evening with M. M. and certainly not after ten months with Harvey. But during the following weeks, I was excluded from discussion groups that took place at Norma Bled's house because Kenny and Ripp thought I was used to better talk.

And why should Norma Bled argue?

I had become M. M.'s property, an empty parking lot with a chain around it, no entry, twenty-four hours a day, seven days a week. I moped and argued with my father and locked myself in the bedroom and lost more weight.

Mother came to the conclusion that there was only one cure:

Minneapolis and the Metropolitan Opera.

8
Millie Moss and the Metropolitan

When Winnipeggers wanted to visit a metropolis, they went south to Minneapolis, only an overnight train trip away. There was no city in Canada, east or west for 1500 miles that could equal Minneapolis for size, shops, and what Zora called the culture factor, which included the Metropolitan Opera touring company as well as restaurants that served Pink Ladies and Creme de Cacao Frappé. Zora barely drank two ounces of alcohol a year, but she felt that restaurants with cocktails had more class than those without.

We had a warm feeling towards the United States and not merely because Manitoba's restaurants were dry and cocktail bars flourished just beyond the U.S. customs stop. The Red River flows north-south and it would have been hard to say where, during my parents' time, Manitoba and Saskatchewan stopped and Minnesota and North Dakota began. People wandered over the border, settled for a few years or longer on the American side, and often returned to become residents of Canada again.

During that long evening at Rabbi Ripp's house when I lost Kenny once again, M. M. had told me that his great grandfather had settled in South Saskatchewan in 1890, a few years later went to Minnesota and stayed there long enough for his son to open a groat mill in St. Paul. After the groat mill failed (Minnesota, unlike Galicia or Bulgaria, was a poor market for groats) the family returned north and settled in Manitoba.

This was typical of the families of most of my friends. People kept a foot on each side of the border, even into the fifties when times were prosperous. Many of the boys in Rabbi Ripp's cultural camp had older brothers in the States and they looked south to their future rather than to eastern Canada. (That is, if Winnipeg wasn't big enough for them.) They found that the United States seemed to need their skills more than Canada and Americans minded less about foreign sounding names. Universities, medical clinics, law firms and accounting offices were expanding all over the south and excellence took priority over the old-boy, old-name network that still existed in Canada.

We looked upon the big eastern cities —.two and one half days away by train — with a sour feeling akin to xenophobia. Financial troubles were blamed on Toronto and many people thought that if Ottawa had given more money for dikes, the big flood of '49 would not have occurred.

The Red River had risen up to the strap room on the second floor of Luxton, my elementary and junior high school. And the Assiniboine was threatening to drown the holy corner in the south end, where St. Mary's Catholic Girls' Academy, the Lutheran Church, and the Shaarey Zedek synagogue stood within a block of each other.

The Normas, the unpopular Carols and I boasted that the worst of the flood's devastation had been at our school. Our feelings were vindicated when Prime Minister Louis St. Laurent came to view the disaster at Luxton. My English teacher, Mr. Gibson, rowed him to the girls' entrance and together they climbed over the sandbags to see the worst. But to no one's great surprise, Mr. St. Laurent, being an eastern man, appeared unmoved by the sight of the Red River lapping by the blackboards and word of his stolid reaction spread. Although Ottawa gave the city a fair proportion of money — some people like Kusy Gwertzman's family were able to improve their flooded houses beyond their original worth — many Winnipeggers preferred to remember what Mr. Gibson said about Mr. St. Laurent: "A cold one. You'd think he sees high water every day swirling around his feet in Parliament."

Montreal was considered almost as far away as Paris. English-speaking Winnipeggers who were of an open mind and believed the French language a graceful addition to general knowledge agreed that one should go to Europe to learn a Parisian French instead of picking up the jargon spoken in Montreal. Decadent old Europe was still the place for frills.

Even the little towns in the States — Fargo, Grand Forks, Duluth — had a glamor that Toronto and Montreal lacked. Everything was open Sunday, bars included, and there were chain stores with cheap goods that didn't exist in Canada. Cheap booze, cheap cigarettes, burlesque shows and cheap shoes. Popular Carol bought, for only $3.95, a pair of imitation red alligator high heels in Grand Forks which could never be found in Winnipeg. Later they dissolved in the rain because the soles were made of paper. But it didn't matter because she had paid so little to look so chic.

Although it was an adventure to go to Grand Forks and Fargo, Minneapolis was the cultural capital of Manitoba. The houses were bigger than any in Western Canada and there were lakes right in the center of the shopping district. No wonder the Metropolitan opera sang there in the flesh once a year. Dayton's Oval room, which sold dresses costing over $200, was just as fine, Emelia Stone reported, as any shop in New York.

What better adventure could there be for Zora,

mother and me to combine bargains from J. C. Penny stores with a little Puccini, as well as a glance at Dayton's, in the Rome of northwestern United States?

Even though I used to hang around Millie Moss Travel and read her folders as escape literature, this was the first time mother would actually give her some business on my account. I hoped that the trip would be therapeutic and I would be cured of thinking about Kenny, Ripp and Norma Bled reading the Kinsey report together. I would rid myself of obsession by shopping (one could buy saddle shoes in the States that just wiped clean instead of having to apply white and dark polish, the Canadian way), eating every meal in a restaurant, and going to the opera in a dress which mother would buy for me at Dayton's.

If I had to tell the truth, I wasn't as excited at going to the opera as I was about shopping. However, Norma Bled and the Carols were impressed and Auntie Zora said the opera was moral justification for the whole trip. But, as I saw it, the trip was to be a refined expensive version of my sweet sixteen, a year earlier. No boys, new kinds of food, plus *Madame Butterfly. Madame Butterfly* was the only opera that affected me. Whenever I heard "One Fine Day," my eyes filled and I found it difficult to sit through the aria without weeping. Ronnie, my brother, claimed that I was the same as the Pavlovian dog salivating at the sound of a bell. He had a point because I was like a stone listening to anything else.

Minneapolis was going to be the most exciting thing in my life. Even though Minneapolis was closer than Toronto, it was still in a foreign country where people spoke in nasal accents and never saw a two-dollar bill. I used to tell the girls that I dreaded the mediocre life most of all. And Winnipeg, we agreed, meant mediocrity. Now my life of mediocrity was going to be abated for several days.

But Zora was anxious about arrangements. Our only difficulty would come from Millie Moss Travel, where we had to make train and hotel reservations.

Millie Moss took over her husband Joe's business — he'd named it after her when they married — when he died of a heart attack. He was then only forty-five but had grown so fat that his heart just couldn't take the strain anymore.

Everyone I knew bought their tickets from Millie Moss Travel. She connected north and south and east and west. Even Emelia Stone went to Millie if she was taking the overnight to Minneapolis. It would have been simpler to buy the tickets at the station but people felt that Millie, a widow, needed the commission more than the Canadian Pacific. A true act of charity because Millie thought that travel was a fool's occupation, at best an escape for the unhappy rich.

My father used to go to Saskatchewan every February to deliver a paper on The South Saskatchewan Oat Crop and Peabody's Rot.

"So what are you running away from this time, Sydney?" she'd say as she made him stand around for an hour making out his train ticket. Millie never traveled herself. We knew for certain that she went to Gimli, sixty miles north of Winnipeg, in a car. She came back with horror stories about fishflies clinging to a stick of salami and a bathing suit stolen right off her cousin's clothesline.

Zora said, "Other than the Gimli trip, Millie's never left Winnipeg. She's never taken a train, or a boat, or a plane. It's natural she gets things mixed up."

It was impossible to make travel arrangements with Millie over the telephone. She always made you come to her office. "I only deal with people in person." If you rang her up and asked her to reserve a seat on the seven o'clock train to Toronto she'd hang up.

Millie Moss Travel was near the CNR station, nestled between two hotels, tawdry pungent places, their open doors exuding smells of beer and urine. The office was dormitory class, no chairs, no display racks, and if you asked for some information about Sicily, she'd come up with a dusty handout about the Florida everglades.

"That's all I've got. It's too hot there too. Give it back when you're finished reading it."

The only ornament in her office was a giant epiphyllum sitting on the worn linoleum platform against the window, a monstrous thing with long thin protuberances, like a green giant's crooked fingers. It sprawled awkwardly over the discolored clay pot and prevented the sun from entering Millie's offices, yet, offering no visual sustenance to the passerby. Except in April. Then thirty or forty buds would appear on the warty grayish cactus and dark pink blossoms with layers of spiky petals sheltering a ray of golden stamens opened to the spring sun. The contrast between the gorgeous flowers and the sickly host that bore them was startling. "How did you get that thing to bloom, Millie?" my mother would ask. She'd shrug her shoulders. "Never look at it from month to month, but in March I sprinkle it with Lux Flakes."

Millie's favorite subject, other than how she killed her husband, was the folly of going first class.

"There's no difference between first and tourist class. You get there the same time whether you sleep on top or below. They don't chop the boat in two, you know, to make first class go faster. And they always feed you. Even dormitory. It's not like when our parents came across the other way, with jars of goose grease."

Emelia Stone was her chief victim. No one traveled as much as Emelia or had more complicated arrangements to make. Millie indignantly recited the itinerary to any loiterer who came into her office.

"Imagine, first class, outside cabin, top deck on the Normandy from New York to Cherbourg. And, of course, Milady needs a private bedroom on the train going from

Winnipeg to New York. And then she thinks that somehow she's going to reach the Nile River, first class."

The Nile expedition was not a success. Millie, true to her principles, tried to save Emelia money and booked her deck passage on a Liberian tramp steamer, for a four-day cruise up the Nile. Harvey Stone told me that the ship was so crowded that she couldn't bribe her way into a first-class cabin and she had to pile her Vuitton luggage around her like an enclosure to keep out a herd of black-faced sheep that were roaming the deck. Once in a while Emelia would make an opening through her leather prison, tiptoe around the sheep droppings and sneak into first class to use the bathroom. But it was no good. They had posted a man by the ladies room just in case some of the riffraff on deck tried to sneak in. As soon as he would see Emelia, he would yell, "Not here missee, you go pee down below. Down, down."

By the time Emelia got off in Khartoum, she was sick. An English doctor told her that it was the first time he saw those particular symptoms in someone who wasn't a Sudanese sheep herder.

Millie's appetite was one of the wonders of Winnipeg. If there was a roasted chicken perched on top of mother's warming oven, Millie could finish it all, without bothering to sit down. If a honey cake sat within reach of her fork, Millie usually remarked, "This is getting dry, Fanny, it's a sin to throw food out." And the cake would disappear in the manner that pleased God. Only three hours earlier, Millie had eaten chili con carne and graham wafer pie at the Salisbury House Coffee Shop near her office.

Yet what was sauce for the goose was poison to the gander. Both she and Joe had loved their food but Millie burned up all her calories while Joe's sluggish metabolism fattened his arteries until they clogged like a dirty drain. But no one could have loved a husband more than Millie.

Every evening Joe used to drive home from Millie

Moss Travel and she'd be waiting for his honk. The neighbors waited as well. Joe pressed on the horn — one long mating call. She'd run outside, in her flapping unzipped galoshes and heave open the heavy garage doors that were stuck in the ice. "I like my Joe to drive in like a gentleman," she told a complaining neighbor. "He works hard all day and deserves a little courtesy."

"The doctor said I killed him with kindness," I once heard her say. "I used to get out of bed in the middle of the night and cook him Red River cereal if he felt hungry. Joe ate it with brown sugar and melted butter. Never cream. And I always had to skim the white bubbles out of the butter."

When Joe had his first attack, the doctor warned Millie that she was caring for him like a blue ribbon pig before the slaughtering. The doctor counseled lettuce leaves, skim milk, and margarine. "Banish butter," he ordered. "Make him walk home from work." Millie might as well have been asked to divorce Joe.

"It makes Joe nauseated to eat Red River cereal with melted margarine. And why should he walk home from work when he's got a car? Look how much I eat and I don't get sick."

Joe's breathing became difficult and his face turned from pale to deep blue in a period of several months. He died, one leg in Millie's lap, while she was tying his shoe laces one day after lunch.

And a decade and a half later, Millie recited every detail of her husband's last mortal hour at the travel office to friends and strangers. "All he ate for dessert were raspberries and skimmed milk. No sugar. And five minutes before he died I ate three of Fanny's cream puffs right in front of him."

At this point in the story, Millie and her customer would have kind of a sixty seconds of silence in honor of Joe's death before business could be resumed.

When Zora made the Minneapolis ticket purchase

she knew that listening to Millie's *mea culpa* narration of Joe's death, even unto mother's cream puffs, would be necessary. Zora feared the usual mismanagement and printed her instructions on lined foolscap paper — a bedroom and a lower berth on the overnight train and twin beds and a cot at the Radisson Hotel. But this was a useless gesture.

When we arrived at the station we found that Millie, true to her principles, had booked us coach. Every bedroom, roomette, and berth was occupied by opera goers who suddenly witnessed a preview, an operatic confrontation between mezzo soprano and basso profundo, as Zora and the CPR conductor quarreled in middle C and low E. Zora sang for pity to the audience in the sleepers, while the conductor stood in the aisle, not looking at Zora, the vexatious prima donna, and concentrated on his aria, a repetition of "Lady there's no place for you in the sleepers, get back to coach." After a final dramatic skirmish, Zora, opening the WC to see if there was room for a berth, realized that she was upstaged and joined mother and me in the wings, in the coach.

Early in the morning, we left the train and eventually found ourselves at the Radisson Hotel, drooping like unwatered begonias, standing beside our surplus suitcases, which we needed for smuggling goods back over the border. We were not surprised when the desk clerk told us he had never heard of us. Millie had ruled out the Radisson because it was a first-class hotel. Instead of at least suggesting a boarding house, Millie, unwilling to confront Zora, simply did not make any reservations at all.

Zora had lost her bedroom on the train but she didn't intend to lose her bedroom at the Radisson. She piled our suitcases in a tower, pulled up a chair in the lobby and told the clerk, "I'm sleeping right here, you will have to call the police to throw me out." Zora's rationale was that, since she had actually gone to a travel agent and requested a room well in advance, it was no business of hers if the booking error had been made by Millie Moss Travel or the hotel. Millie wasn't around to blame; therefore the hotel was at fault. Mother believed that desk clerks must be obeyed and creating scenes in lobbies was a crime, yet she realized that hotel rooms were unprocurable during the opera season and feared that she would have to bed her only daughter in the Salvation Army Hostel. Rattled by Zora's behavior, panicking at the vision of me sleeping under the same roof as an unwed mother, she ran to the Radisson coffee shop as soon as Zora began fooling with the suitcases.

When Zora started moving furniture in the lobby to make herself a couch, I joined mother, who was trying to hide her loss of control at the coffee shop counter.

"Have some coffee, Verna," she said, trying to sound brighter, covering up a gargle sob in her throat. "You never get a bad cup of coffee in the States."

Mother knew that new things to eat and drink might divert me. I would be comforted while we waited for the police to come and drag Zora away. Mother was right, the coffee was better than in Winnipeg and the menu offered jelly omelettes, sticky buns with pecans and caramel, and sweet relishes and cottage cheese with everything, even at breakfast. She was desperate enough to urge me to try stuffed avocado with crab meat, a novelty for me, as an appetizer to the wheatcake.

Before I ordered, Zora walked in.

"Cowards," she brayed, "the bellboy has taken our luggage up to the presidential suite. We're staying there for three days and the price is the same as for the room Millie should have reserved. Leave it to me girls. I win 99.99 percent of the time. I told that little desk clerk that the presidential suite was sure to be empty because Eisenhower is visiting troops in Europe, a million miles away from Minneapolis."

Zora believed that presidential suites across the

nation remained empty in readiness for Eisenhower or Zora to move in. The desk clerk had obviously caved in to Zora's line of reasoning. The suite was dove gray and the presidential twin beds were hidden from the curious by a velvet curtain. There were two bathrooms, three gray telephones, three television sets, and an empty liquor cabinet. But as much as we loved the appointments, Hennepin Avenue was outside, with shops that sold Capezio shoes, red plastic ketchup containers shaped like tomatoes, and percale sheets, which cost one-third less than in Canada. We took enough time to shower before we went on the town.

The performance of *Madame Butterfly* was taking place the same night. Mother had even bought me a rayon taffeta, off-the-shoulder dress that had been hanging on the half price rack in the Oval Room, and a strapless bra reinforced by wire ribbing which would leave me scarred for several years. I knew that if I didn't feel the wire biting in my flesh it meant that the bra had slipped to my midriff and I would look as if I was wearing a moneybelt under my dress. Pain was my guide to elegance. As soon as I felt the pressure from the wires ease I hitched up each side of the brassiere so the metal settled back into the ridges imbedded in my skin.

Auntie Zora had come with us to Minneapolis because it was her twenty-fifth wedding anniversary and she felt that she deserved a treat. Gerald didn't accompany us because he disliked opera and had nothing to buy. The last time Gerald went with Zora he irritated her by staying in the hotel room most of the time and calculating if Zora had really made a saving on her purchases, since the Canadian dollar was worth less than the American. On this trip, silver anniversary or no, Zora left Gerald, the killjoy, at home to grind his lenses. Still, Zora wanted to mark the day in a special way, so she bought three identical gardenia corsages for us to wear in honor of the occasion. Mother wore hers on the wrist because she was short-waisted and couldn't take too much fussiness up front. Zora, who was tall, wore the gardenia pinned to her shoulder and both of them labored for an hour in the presidential suite with bobby pins and silver paper so that my gardenia would stay put in my hair. Zora at last pronounced the flower as secure as Dorothy Lamour's and paid for our cab to the opera.

Our seats were in the balcony and mother brought along an old pair of opera glasses to see *Butterfly* up close. After a glance at the stage, I scanned the audience and pointed out familiar faces, Winnipeggers, to Zora and mother. Emelia Stone was sitting in the third row orchestra, wearing subdued gray lace, next to her cousin, a Minneapolis judge. Zora said he must be corrupt because American judges were elected. Emelia's cousin had to spend his days grabbing votes — eating swedish limpa and vinerterta at the Viking Clubs — instead of studying up on wise judicial decisions, like Canadian judges, who were appointed. "You're either a judge or a politician, not both."

My favorite moment at the opera was intermission and I wandered about in my gardenia and strapless taffeta, happy and confident. I had lost some pounds over the past months and as long as I kept hitching up the bra I looked like anyone else. Mother and Zora were talking to Emelia and her cousin in the lobby — Zora was repeating her views on elected judges — while the others listened, the judge a little red in the face.

I had slipped away from them daydreaming my way to the water fountain. A voice whispered behind me, almost in my gardenia.

It was Kenny. Wearing a suit, holding an opera program, and standing alone. A miracle, a mystery. What was the milkman's son, the only boy I ever loved and always would, doing at the Minneapolis Met? My confidence (taffeta dress and strapless bra just hitched up) was strong enough to permit me to believe that Kenny had followed me to Minneapolis so we could avoid the rubber-necking of Norma Bled. I mentally dropped my plans for shopping with Zora and mother and was indifferent to the big dinner at Charlie's restaurant, promised for the following evening. Kenny and I would go to the art gallery, the libraries and the museums, and Zora and mother could buy what they wanted at the J. C. Penney stores. Capezio shoes meant nothing to me now.

"What are you doing here Kenny?" I replied.

He sort of nibbled on a knuckle and said nothing. He couldn't admit of course that he was looking for me.

"Are you staying in Minneapolis long?" I persisted.

"A couple more days. I'm seeing three operas, *Tosca* and *Rigoletto* as well as *Madame Butterfly*."

Mother had only bought tickets for this evening because of the expense. It was sloppy thinking on Kenny's part filling our evenings with opera without checking to see if I would be going to all of them. I wondered where he found the money. My confidence began to ebb.

"Are any of the other boys here?" I asked.

"No, no, none of the guys came down."

I was still suspicious. "I suppose Norma is seeing all three operas too."

"Norma?" Kenny was puzzled. "Norma's not here. At least I haven't seen her."

I was relieved. My first instincts must be correct. I became as bold as I had ever been with him. If Kenny came to Minneapolis to be with me he needed encouragement.

"What are your plans for tomorrow?"

"Oh, maybe a few art galleries and the museum."

He didn't ask me to come with him, but then Kenny was so shy. I tried to help.

"I might be going to the museum tomorrow. What time will you be going?"

Kenny was silent, but he was noted for his pauses. Kusy said that Kenny's sentences contained more pauses than words.

"I'm not exactly sure. It doesn't depend on me."

Just then the curtain bell rang and he said, "See you later," and disappeared into the orchestra seats. I stood there trying to divine the words, "It doesn't depend on me." Were they a timid but gallant way of letting me set the hour and then frightened by his temerity, Kenny had run away? Or was he with someone else?

I ran upstairs to my seat and grabbed the opera glasses from Zora. The lights were still on and I desperately tried to pick out Kenny down below. But people who were still filing into their seats obscured my view.

Zora said, "I saw you talking to that Kenny, the one who crashed your sweet sixteen last year. I didn't know his father was doing so well."

I turned to her. "What do you mean?"

"It costs a lot of money for a young man to come to Minneapolis and to the opera. He must get the money from somewhere. Maybe his father's bought a dairy or something."

I knew that Kenny's father still went the rounds with his horse and cart. Norma told me that Kenny delivered the milk on summer mornings. I shrugged. Mother and Zora knew nothing about my feeling for Kenny and that's how I wanted it.

Zora retrieved the glasses.

"Well look who's there. Rabbi Ripp. I wonder where his wife is? She needs a rest, poor thing, all those diapers and children. A trip to Minneapolis should perk her up. I hope he buys her some decent clothes while they're here. She always looks as if she just climbed out of the laundry chute."

Zora continued peering through the glasses.

"Will you look at that. He's sitting beside that Kenny. And the seats on either side of them are taken by strangers. Where's Mrs. Ripp?"

I pulled away the glasses from Zora. Kenny and Ripp were talking to each other, their heads close together. Mrs. Ripp was certainly in Winnipeg. The men had come together and Ripp must have paid Kenny's way. That's what Kenny meant, "It doesn't depend on me."

I was disappointed. Ripp was better than Norma Bled but he would certainly be a hindrance to the sight-seeing I planned to do with Kenny. I wondered if Ripp minded if I went with them. I must be intellectual enough for Rabbi Ripp by now; after all, I had captivated M. M. Maybe he'd even let Kenny and me, being young and un-married, go off alone.

Zora and mother were whispering.

"Don't be ridiculous," mother was saying to Zora, "after all he's married and has all those children. He even adopted the Japanese."

Zora argued, "He's with that young boy. Not his wife. It must be terrible for her. No wonder she looks like a kicked cat."

"I don't believe such a thing exists. The newspapers make it all up. And Sydney says there's a law against it."

"Nonsense, I bet my bottom dollar he paid for that boy's trip. Only a pansy would do that."

I stared at her. "What are you talking about?"

Mother's face got the crumply look. "Keep quiet, Zora, you say crazy things sometimes. Don't listen to her, Verna."

Zora ignored mother. "You'll have to let her grow up sometime. We were just wondering why Ripp would take that Kenny up to Minneapolis instead of his wife, who looks as if she's ready for a breakdown. It's not normal."

I repeated, "What do you mean, pansy?"

I knew that pansies were supposed to be extremely feminine men who became hairdressers and sometimes dressed in women's clothes. Ronnie, who was a medical student, said they had an underdeveloped set of female organs along with male things; they were really her-maphrodites and were to be pitied. Pansies couldn't have children. Rabbi Ripp had three, and one adopted. And

Kenny wasn't feminine in any way. His shoulders were broader than any of the other boys.

I was appalled by Zora's assumptions and sided with my mother. "I don't know what you're talking about."

The only thing I had heard about homosexuals was the Vescio case, in Winnipeg after the war. Three newsboys had been murdered and the whole city was on guard for their children. At the time, when mother expressed worry about my safety, Lord Rex Winograd had snorted and said, "It's Ronnie you have to worry about. The murderer is a pansy. He only attacks boys."

I couldn't understand what Zora meant. But it was peculiar that Rabbi Ripp took Kenny along instead of his wife. No one I knew in Winnipeg would ever do a thing like that. I could imagine five men going away on a fishing trip together. But opera was female domain and if a man did go to the opera he always took his wife. Some of the unmarried boys used to come up seven to a Chevrolet, ostensibly to see the opera. But everyone knew they really came to Minneapolis to cruise the American girls, who were fast and sexy.

This business of Rabbi Ripp and Kenny was beyond my imagination. I partly shared my mother's belief that such a vice did not exist. On the other hand, if there was a law against it, perhaps Zora knew something my mother didn't. I stared down at Ripp and Kenny and wondered if Kenny had to sit on Ripp's lap or something, as a kind of payment for the Minneapolis trip. The idea was ludicrous but worrying.

I decided not to look for Kenny during the next intermission. Even if Zora was wrong and there was an innocent reason for the two of them being together, my confidence had vanished. Besides, mother would not like me going to art galleries with suspected pansies — even though she said the whole thing was made up by the newspapers. I knew I had to push Kenny out of my mind entirely and concentrate on good marks, buying Capezio shoes and being nicer to the unpopular Carols.

Homosexuality was a confusing idea but I understood one thing that frightened me. If Zora was right, I had no place in the Ripp-Kenny relationship. Inevitably I would be rejected and I had no strength to withstand rejection from anyone. Especially from the boy I would be in love with all my life.

After our return from Minneapolis, Zora's interest in Rabbi Ripp's alleged perversion continued and she urged mother to consult the only person who knew about such things: Cousin Rex.

9
Lord
Rex
Winograd

One member of our family turned the rest of us into hypocrites: cousin Rex Winograd. We would criticize and crab about everything he did. My father was disgusted by those bloated carp, "sewer fish," floating in Rex's aquarium. My mother disapproved of Noreen, his girlfriend, who sang songs like "Love for Sale" at La Cucaracha Night Club on Pembina Highway. "She's beneath Rex," a statement that never failed to bring on a snicker from Ronnie.

Face to face with Rex, however, we toadied and treated him with the deference and wariness that loyal family retainers reserve for the young duke.

There was no one else like him. He broke all the rules and was never punished. Rex could take Noreen to my mother's for Saturday lunch and she'd knock herself out making his favorite dishes: bean and barley soup, blueberry pie, and boiled chicken, which the rest of us hated. Rex liked heavy birds, tinged with yellow, whose flesh remained solid after a long forgetful boiling. One drumstick from such a fowl, the thick glutinous skin loosened but still tenaciously clinging to the meat, was enough to satisfy Rex if there was soup and pie as well. After supper, mother would offer Noreen cups of tea in the Aynsley china, with little linen napkins, as if she was my school principal.

Rex's house on Wellington Crescent (highest taxes in the city) had embellishments rare in Winnipeg. The most unusual was his aquarium conservatory. Black-nosed and wattled eel pouts, tiger fish and dreamers flicked back and forth in greenish tanks of water among waving algae stirred up by the bubbling of the oxygen hose. Citrus trees full of fruit and flower, giant hibiscus, and shining Japanese fatsias faced the windows and the January snow, indifferent to the winter weather.

A goldfish pond, or rather a trench, had been carved out of a corner of the far side of the room but the goldfish were always eaten up by the carp that disgusted my father. Rex shared nothing in common, habits, attitudes or even appearances with the rest of the family, except one: an interest in cooking. His specialty was carp soup. "Even that," my father said, "is an abnormal taste."

His cooking sprees were spontaneous midnight events and he needed fresh fish on hand. Rex was an insomniac; only the labor of killing and cleaning the carp, mincing the onions and cubing potatoes put him to sleep. If that was insufficient, he would make up a batter and fry jelly busters for dessert.

Most rose lovers prefer hybrid teas because they are tall, handsome and, in rose growers' terminology, "repeatedly showy." Rex Winograd was a hybrid who fitted all three categories. His mother was Fiona McNabb, daughter of Dr. Hector NcNabb, a dour but capable surgeon who lived a seemly and restrained life in the south end of the city. Fiona, lacking her father's sense of fitness and judgment, married, at an early age, my Great Uncle Boris, an indolent and melancholic photographer of Russian-Jewish parentage who had inherited the temperament if not the talent of a nineteenth century slavic artiste. Great Uncle Boris was no catch even for the daughters of ethnics teeming in the north end. He only stirred from his daydream, before and after marriage, to photograph still lifes of eggs. He earned a small living from taking and tinting wedding and graduation pictures but his soul yearned after absolute purity of form, manifested by the egg's consistent shape.

Understandably, Dr. MacNabb banished Fiona from his inglenook and, two years after her marriage, and one year after Rex's birth, Fiona was taken to Selkirk, a town twenty-five miles north of Winnipeg, where they had a hospital for people who "went mental."

My father said that given Rex's mad, mixed heritage we should be thankful he wasn't a murderer. "Of course," he would add, "with him you can never tell."

Rex didn't seem to care about anything yet he was a success in life. Ordinary people, accountants, furriers, and hardware store owners, stopped talking and listened with respect when Rex's name was mentioned. An objective observer, Mendel Glow, the big-time caterer who had no blood ties with our family, spoke of him as one of the merchant princes of Winnipeg. Rex was always talking secrets with the most important person at the party, plotting industrial putsches that would affect more members of the Kiwanis Club than you'd care to mention.

I don't know how Rex got to be a big shot. All I ever heard from my family were his failures. He took over my grandfather's small lumberyard a year after his death and branched out in other directions, including buying a chinchilla farm where the animals refused to mate, and selling squirrel capes on wire hangers from the back of his lumberyard truck. He even tried to convince Great Uncle Miller to build a miniature golf course on his farmland. That failed too. But by the time he was forty, Rex had become a true wheeler dealer, exchanged the pickup truck for a Rolls Royce and had given Noreen a wild mink coat for her birthday.

My father tried to maintain a modicum of sarcasm in Rex's presence. "Well Big Shot, have you reached the top of Dun and Bradstreet yet?" Rex would reach into his breast pocket, withdraw a piece of twisted tissue paper and fling the contents on the dining table without even bothering to look at my father. A dozen or so diamonds of varying sizes tumbled beside the tea cup, not one of them nearly as small as my mother's engagement ring, bought twenty-five years after her marriage.

"These seeds won't rust," Rex challenged my father. At that, Daddy would go to the sun room for the rest of the evening and brood over the *Rust Journal* and a cup of tea.

"I didn't find those diamonds in Rosebud, Saskatchewan, you bet your life," Rex said to my mother. "A Chinaman living in a hole on Hastings Avenue sold them to me cheap. He'd just come off the boat in Vancouver, smuggled them out of Shanghai. I bought them because they're liquid. Never be too sure of anybody or anything, least of all governments. Just try and sell stocks and bonds when Canada goes Communist."

Aunt Zora, so forceful in her own conversation and so easily bored by others, especially "masculine-megalomaniac-stock-and-bond talk," was as enchanted as Desdemona hearing from Othello when Rex told tales about himself. She would shriek with laughter when Rex described how he boiled his dirty socks in the cabbage borsht that he cooked especially for some hunting cronies at his Lockport Lodge on the Red River. Or how, during a fishing trip, he had hidden behind an elderberry bush while his army friend Gordie Teakles was defecating in the woods, stuck out a shovel at the right moment from behind and withdrew the feces before his friend was able to turn around and confirm his act. "Gordie went nuts. He peered under every blueberry bush, lifted every pine branch and kept shoving around leaves for about an hour. I said 'You lose something, Gordie?' He finally must have figured that he had a hallucination about crapping."

When Rex was generous he liked it to show. He gave my grandmother a solid silver, hand-chased punch bowl, two feet across. ("Came from the late Queen Mary's collection, sold to pay off a blackmailer") and four dozen matching goblets. Granny had a three-room apartment, or suite as it was called in Winnipeg, and the goblets took up the space remaining from the artificial daffodils, tinted photographs of grandchildren, and bonbon dishes filled with Woolworth's licorice niblets. The punch bowl was in the place of honor, on the card table covered by a madeira lace cloth, also Rex's gift, where Granny served meals. It looked as if she was having a perpetual punch party, although I never remember any fluid other than silver polish poured into the goblets or the bowl.

Granny's suite would only have taken up one corner of Rex's sunken living room. On the south wall of this room, a local artist had painted a mural stretching from the polar bear rugs on the floor to the cathedral ceiling inlaid with maccassar ebony, mahogany, walnut and carpathian burled elm. The mural depicted Rex in his favorite outfit, at first glance just riding boots and jodhpurs, but, to the more knowledgeable, the Royal Canadian Army cavalry dress. Rex wore it everywhere without second thought — when he went to a board meeting at the hospital or to the Bank of Montreal to negotiate a loan. He was painted squarely in the center of the mural, holding a blueprint in one hand and pointing to a monumental project with the other, much in the manner of Ferdinand de Lesseps directing the construction of the Suez Canal. This, no doubt, was the local artist's conception of Rex at work, aided by Rex's own description of the daily humdrum of his life.

Every table, every lamp in Rex's house was made of driftwood, a decorating craze that had a deservedly short popularity in the early fifties. He had found a warehouse full of these objects in Montreal and believed that every Winnipegger would share his passion for them at five hundred dollars a crack. He shipped the lot home and a few people who owed Rex money found them irresistible, but everyone else, including my mother, balked at furnishing their houses with a gnarled and twisted five-foot tree trunk with a lucite lamp shade perched on its farthest spike.

Zora continued to urge mother to consult Cousin Rex about Rabbi Ripp and Kenny. But Rex Winograd was not a man to come at anyone's beck and call, least of all mother's or Zora's. Lord Rex kept aloof and only descended among the family as *deus ex machina* when he decided that our mortal erring had led us down a blind alley. Rex, kin to Scotch dukes and a local merchant prince in his own right, always complained when he led us back to the good path, "You Winograd people can't dress yourselves in the morning without calling me to pull up the zippers."

About three weeks after the Minneapolis trip and many pleading calls from mother, Rex concluded that his leadership was needed and walked into our house just before midnight, his usual visiting hour. As soon as he arrived, Father went upstairs to bed and mother began to make scones to go with his tea. I was gratified when Rex motioned me to stay by him. "Stick around, Verna, I have a proposition that can make or break you." Rex had a purpose in coming to see us, other than explaining the ins and outs of pederasty to mother.

My heart pumped and I was happy that he had not taken offense because I turned down the debutante offer.

After that episode, we hadn't heard from Rex for several months, except through Ronnie. Cousin Rex often called on him at medical school and took him to the beer parlor because Ronnie had to learn what men did. During their conversations (most of which, Ronnie said, would not be interesting to me) Rex had urged Ronnie to go in for a medical specialty like surgery or radiology, which were money-makers. "You're going to need it kid with a spinster sister to support for the rest of your days." I was pleased and surprised that Cousin Rex still believed that I had some potential left in life.

However, mother and I had Rabbi Ripp and Kenny on our minds. Before Cousin Rex could come forth with my chance of a lifetime, mother brought up the subject of Rabbi Ripp with, as she put it, "a handsome young boy, no names mentioned, in Minneapolis." Rabbi Ripp had not been uppermost in Rex's mind, but he listened with interest as mother described, with much hesitation, the scene at the opera house. Mother disliked making moral judgments.

"It was Zora," she said, "who thought Ripp should not have been there with the young man."

Rex had no doubts.

"I knew there was something funny about Ripp. He owes money all over town. The books he reads make a kakaputzi of his brains. I'll call the president of the university tomorrow and get him fired. Mind you he'll be lucky not to go to jail. They hung Vescio."

Rex looked at me. "Verna, don't horse around with men who read too much. They'll just pass their headaches on to you."

Mother had merely wanted Rex's opinion of Ripp's behavior; the idea of putting Ripp in jail made her frantic. She hadn't thought that her gossiping to Rex would result in such severe action.

She backtracked, seeing Mrs. Ripp with three children plus the Japanese on her doorstep with a begging bowl.

"Please don't call the president, Rex. I've no proof. And Zora exaggerates everything. Leave things as they are."

She put her hand on Rex's arm, like Brutus' wife beseeching her husband to stay the slaying of her sons.

I don't know if Rex really meant to call the president or if he even knew him. Rex liked saying things like that. He relished these intimations of secret power and contacts in high places. Mother was awed by Rex, but Daddy and Ronnie were skeptical. Ronnie once told mother that

Cousin Rex bragged a lot. But she turned on Ronnie, "If you do as well as Rex in life, Ronnie, then you can brag too."

Rex was the kind of person who let one idea drive him for weeks. Whatever was paramount in his mind pushed aside lesser things, like getting Ripp fired, no matter how satisfying.

"Listen, Fanny, fruitcakes aren't my problem. I don't have any sons to worry about. If you, a mother, want to let perverts on the campus that's fine with me. What good are universities anyhow? I've done all right without."

Mother was not satisfied with this answer but with Rex it was all or nothing. It was better to let Rabbi Ripp take young boys to Minneapolis than be responsible for putting him in jail.

Rex announced that he had something on his mind that was more important than the suspicion that Ripp was a pansy.

"You haven't heard. I'm opening a restaurant. It's going to be the equal to the finest in the States, better than Charlie's in Minneapolis and just as good as the Brown Derby in L. A. The place is being redecorated right now, inside and out. I expect to serve 200 tables a night, and there's going to be a dance orchestra Fridays and Saturdays. The dinnerware costs a fortune, imported from Denmark, and the glass is so heavy you need two hands for lifting. All the waitresses are wearing peasant blouses and wide skirts and Verna that's where you come in. If you work at my place Saturday nights, you can earn enough in tips to take a dozen trips to Minneapolis. What do you do Saturday nights anyhow? Sit at home and make fudge with the girls? No future in that."

I was disappointed. Being a waitress wasn't nearly as classy as turning into a debutante. I had let that one slip through my fingers. Cousin Rex had certainly lowered his opinion of me. Before I could respond, Rex continued.

"Unlike your husband, Fanny, I have vision.

Remember I put money into the first shopping mall in Winnipeg against Great Uncle Miller's advice and made myself more than Sydney will ever see in his lifetime. I know this restaurant will work. I feel it in my bones. There's going to be a desire for spaghetti *without* meatballs, plus pizza, that will sweep this continent. And I want to be in on the ground floor." (Rex's visions were not only profit oriented. In 1948, he dreamt about a man walking on the moon, "with difficulty, dragging his feet.")

"Of course, Verna, you know damn all about waitressing. But that doesn't matter. Noreen will train you in. She's going to run the place with her family. They've been in the restaurant business for years. What her father doesn't know about the food business isn't worth a fart in a windstorm."

I had already refused the debutante party and felt Rex would never have anything more to do with me if I refused this fire sale offer. I accepted immediately although I was not happy about being under Noreen's tutelage. She was thin and beautiful and made me feel awkward as soon as she entered the room. "Verna's trouble," as my parents referred to my inferiority complex, was always extreme when Noreen was around. I was bothered by another feeling of which I was ashamed as well as my IC: snobbishness. Noreen's background was unorthodox. Mother, Zora and father believed that her respectability was fragile and entirely dependent upon her association with Rex.

Noreen was half Ukrainian, half Chinese, with the height and honey-colored hair of her mother and the slenderness and high cheekbones of her father. Rex found her singing torch songs at La Cucaracha Night Club and fell in love instantly. They went everywhere together, and for fifteen years the two hybrids were indubitably the handsomest couple in Winnipeg. Zora said, grudgingly, that Rex looked like a young Hemingway and Noreen definitely was Garboesque, but with slantier eyes.

Noreen's father owned a small café, the Bide a Wee Eats, near the railway station, that specialized in hot chicken sandwiches. (Less of a go-getter than other Chinese immigrants, Mr. Lee never seized upon the fact that ancestral fare like sweet and sour spare ribs or even moo goo guy pan might have commercial value.) Noreen's mother had been the Bide a Wee waitress, but after ten years of wiping off counters and slopping gravy over chips she ran off to Flin Flon with a Finnish lumberjack leaving Noreen behind.

By the time Rex came into her life, Noreen was fairly well known. Her name occasionally appeared in advertisements for La Cucaracha in the entertainment section of the newspapers and she used to model part-time for Eatons. Rex liked to be seen with Noreen in public places, like Rae and Jerry's steak house and the horse races at Polo Park. She dressed like a French model, every tuck and seam followed the movement of her body. Not that she looked as if she was poured into her clothes; quite the contrary, like true couture dresses they obeyed her body's commands. Her proportions were as delicate as those of any filly on the course. Noreen had a Chinese aunt who lived in the back of the café who could copy a Dior creation just by looking at a picture in Harper's Bazaar.

Although Rex took Noreen most places, even to my mother's house, he avoided larger functions, especially weddings. He did not want to marry Noreen. He delighted in flaunting and shocking, in castigating others for their narrowness and mediocrity, but in his heart of hearts, he felt that he deserved a more respectable girl.

The family, however, had come to accept Noreen and even saw some virtue in the liaison.

Mother admitted that Noreen didn't slurp her soup and put up with Rex's irregular hours and egomania in a way that few girls from more conventional families would have managed to do. We might have forgiven Noreen her background if it hadn't been for her conversation. She would sidle up to Zora or me and whisper in her baby doll voice, "I weigh 105. What do you weigh?" And sometimes she'd take a tape measure from her purse and measure herself in front of everyone. "Thirty-four, twenty-two, thirty-six. Now it's your turn," and she'd hand the tape measure over to Zora. Zora and I could spare at least four inches anywhere from neck to calf, and our weight was a secret, especially from ourselves.

Zora answered always, "Serious people don't bother about such vain things. I don't know and I don't care." But she did and so did I.

Rex was proud when Noreen's picture appeared in the woman's page modeling a gown from Eaton's import room and he'd listen night after night to her small voice trilling *Blue Tango* and *Perfidia* at La Cucaracha. But during their fifteen years together, he never mentioned marriage.

His relationship with Noreen was, nevertheless, sanctified, in a way, by the manager of the Higgins and Main branch of the Bank of Montreal when he borrowed money from the bank to open the restaurant. He hired the only experts he knew in the field, the Bide a Wee staff, Mr. Lee and the aunt who sewed (she was also gravy maker for the hot chicken sandwiches), as maitre d' and chef. Noreen was to be hostess-entertainer when she wasn't busy modeling, or singing at La Cucaracha. As far as she was concerned, this was the next best thing to marriage. Rex trusted her family with his money. How many husbands had that much confidence in their in-laws?

Rex only made one stipulation. The restaurant had to serve Italian food.

From the start, Zora was skeptical. "How can a Chinese counterman from Main Street, whose silent partner is half Jew, half Scotch, make money serving ravioli to

Winnipeggers like your father, who only orders roast beef well done in restaurants?" This was the question in all our minds.

I had faith in Rex's vision if Zora didn't and next Saturday afternoon I presented myself at the House of Norograd (from Noreen and Winograd). Noreen was already dressed for the evening in a flowered skirt with three tiers of flounces, black velvet bodice and a Spanish comb in her hair. Ethnically speaking, her outfit was more reminiscent of gypsy caves near Seville than Sicilian peasants and Funiculi Funicula. No matter, few Winnipeggers would nitpick. Noreen told me that because of her senior position as hostess-waitress she had to wear something that would single her out from the rest of the help, like the maid of honor from the bridesmaids. The rest of the help, including me, wore pink nylon smocks that Rex had bought from a bankrupt beauty salon. They were all late forties boxy, with shoulders pads, and had been made from war surplus parachutes.

"You won't be starting out as a waitress the first month anyhow," Noreen instructed me. "You'll have to begin as busboy, scrape the dirty dishes, take away from tables, and help the dishwashers in the kitchen. If you do OK Rex will promote you."

More than half of the restaurant was still under construction and the 200 tables that Rex had spoken of had not yet materialized. Instead there were tarpaulins, two-by-fours and step ladders. The unfinished section was separated by a huge screen painted by the same hand that had depicted Rex as pharoah's overseer in his Wellington Crescent mural. The picture on the screen showed Rex in a toreador outfit and Noreen in her Carmen dress holding out their arms in a welcoming gesture. Artificial clusters of grapes were strung across the ceiling of the habitable part of the restaurant and pink arborite tables and a large barrel stamped Vinho, made up the rest of the decor, except for the lamps, which were remnants from Rex's driftwood collection.

The help had been recruited from Noreen's Chinese relations — three older women, including the aunt who sewed. Her father, wearing a chef's hat irritably supervised their doings, screaming at the women in Cantonese as they scuttled about.

"We only need one waiter right now because the restaurant isn't finished," Noreen explained.

"The kitchen women can do double duty and help at the tables. We hired a guy who's had a lot of experience in dealing with the public. He's never waited on tables, mind you, but he knows the food trade — specialized in dairy products. Dad wanted his cousin who's a trained waiter to take the job but Rex believes a Chinese up front would make everyone think this is just another chop house. The guy we hired gets to wear an Italian costume. Same as me. He's changing behind the screen."

A familiar pair of broad shoulders emerged clad in an unfamiliar white blouse with puffed sleeves and velvet vest with silver buttons. Kenny had a red rayon sash around his waist and black toreador pants.

"You two will be seeing a lot of each other so I guess I better introduce you."

Kenny gave me the usual Mona Lisa smile and we said in unison that we were old friends.

My confusion over Kenny's sexual leaning increased as I stared at his outfit and I resolutely put a restaurant romance out of my mind. Noreen, however, seemed to like the way he looked.

"Real cute kid. You'll knock the girlies dead. We've got a regular Valentino here, Verna."

Kenny blushed and told Noreen that she looked lovely in the costume. He didn't say anything about my pink parachute.

Customers dribbled in, not many, but enough to keep

us fairly busy. I chopped cabbage, tried to understand Noreen's father's instructions about where to put garbage and walked around the restaurant with a plastic trolly gathering dirty plates from the tables. Noreen wrote down the orders, yelled them out in Cantonese to the kitchen ladies and slowly carried out one plate of spaghetti at a time, so nothing would spill on her dress. Later in the evening, a man played an accordion and Noreen left her waitress duties and sang "Come Back to Sorrento." Kenny had little trouble catching on to the intricacies of his duties and even pulled back the chairs for the ladies when they left.

The next few weeks were relatively uneventful, except for the time Kenny had to run after a lady who tried to steal the Vinho barrel. She had rolled it out of the door of the restaurant and Kenny only caught sight of her bent figure through the window as she pushed the barrel down Pembina Highway. He ran after her and promised not to call the police if she allowed him to roll the barrel back in the restaurant. She agreed with some argument.

When I decided that Kenny only fell in love with men I felt less edgy in his presence. There were many things I could do to make myself more attractive to men but I could not change myself into one. It would do no good even if I was smarter and thinner. Miss America with a Ph.D. would leave Kenny cold. It was a relief to know that Verna Plumpling, from Machray Street, was not personally responsible for Kenny's lack of interest. This homosexual thing was bigger than both of us.

We were buddies. He helped me scrape the dirty dishes and I kept an eye out for "dine and dashers" — the people who left without paying while Kenny or Noreen were looking the other way. Once Kenny hopped on a bus and traveled ten blocks to confront a couple who dined and dashed with their bill. They finally paid but he had to walk back and three other tables had left in disgust, waiting for him to return. The House of Norograd had a dine and dash case at least twice a week. Noreen didn't particularly like the waitressing but as long as she could sing a few songs in the evening and wear the costume she felt her prestige was still intact. Noreen was a tolerant girl and appreciated Kenny's efforts in collecting bills. The House of Norograd wasn't Maxims or the Brown Derby, but we still got on well together and Noreen's dad only screamed at his relations in the kitchen. The main problem was the absence of customers.

Rex, like many visionaries, was right too soon: it was still the pre-pizza era. He had foresight but his timing was wrong. If he had opened the House of Norograd a few years later with a staff from Calabria instead of Canton, he might have stayed out of trouble.

And everyone agreed that the restaurant's name was ethnically confusing.

Zora said, "Norograd does not sound like spaghetti. It sounds like borscht. North Winnipeggers eat enough borscht in their own homes."

Even so, the House of Norograd might have seen better times if it were not for the Coca Cola bottles and Noreen's dead dog.

At that time it was still against the law to serve alcohol, even wine and beer, with meals at a public restaurant. Most Manitobans drank steadily but surreptitiously from bottles of rye hidden in paper bags under their table. Set ups: soda water, ginger ale and ice, sat on the table and were provided by the restaurant at a price. The law was very strict. A small Hungarian restaurant across the street from Zora's house was fined out of existence for serving liqueur chocolates as a Christmas bonus.

Rex was cosmopolitan and loved to drink wine with his food. He hid his homemade wine in the furnace room at the restaurant and served the stuff in Coca Cola bottles (the color was the same as Coca Cola) but only to "special friends." It was a heavy, sugary, sacramental kind of wine with a high alcoholic content. He never charged any money for it, he just wanted people to tell him how good it was.

About a year after the House of Norograd had opened, one of the "special friends," who must have owed Rex money, tipped off the Mounties. Six constables walked into the restaurant, collected all the pop bottles from the diners' tables, even the Orange Crush some children were drinking, and then went directly to the furnace room in the basement.

Rex probably would have got away with a fine since this was his first offence. But matters were complicated by Noreen's bulldog. A week before the raid, Perfect Furs had sent Noreen on a modeling trip to Regina. Plug, her fourteen-year-old bulldog, had died while she was away. Noreen's father knew that she would take the death very hard if she wasn't able to view the remains. Instead of getting rid of the animal immediately, the aunt who sewed bound its limbs while the body was still warm, wrapped it in brown butcher's paper, like a rolled rib of beef, and put it on the middle shelf of the walk-in freezer, next to the packages of chicken giblets and hamburger meat, to stay fresh until Noreen's return.

Rex's wine, without a doubt, could be frozen and defrosted without serious alteration, and although it wasn't stored in the freezer, the Mounties thought they'd better have a look. They didn't find wine, but they did unwrap Plug.

Illicit distilleries are nothing next to the Yellow Peril. Here indeed was proof positive of the white man's fears of the oriental. A fourteen-year-old bulldog, oven ready, obviously waiting its turn to go into the chop suey, to be served to occidental innocents. Even worse, the animal wasn't even slaughtered in an abattoir like a healthy calf. It had, as Mr. Lee explained, knocking another nail in the "Closed" sign of the House of Norograd, died of old age and disease.

That was the end of Rex's vision. The House of Norograd was shut down, boarded up and held in escrow by the Bank of Montreal.

I think Noreen was relieved not to carry plates of spaghetti around, even without meatballs. Perhaps she was reminded of her mother sliding hot turkey sandwiches down the counter at the Bide a Wee for so many years. When we worked together, Noreen used to say that the Bide a Wee was a dump and Norograd was a class joint. But still she must have had a few nostalgic moments when her dad used the Bide a Wee recipe for gravy and a can of tomatoes to create the House of Norograd's famous sauce.

Rex never looked back at anything in his life. He had new ventures and more money to make elsewhere. He said, however, that he had signed statements in his safe that proved that the four constables were on the take. He was just waiting for the right moment to let hell break loose.

10
The Hump
Gets Heavier

My father was not upset by the fall of the House of Norograd. Subsequently, vandals raided the premises and threw the disappointingly empty Vinho kegs against the bay window facing the highway and set fire to the unfinished portion of the restaurant. The fire was caught in time by a cruising policeman but smoke darkened the yellow clapboard and the firemen had to break down the front door. Nothing gave father greater pleasure than driving along Pembina and pointing out Rex's dilapidated folly to visiting relations from the States.

Daddy never believed my future lay with the restaurant business; as a matter of fact, he disliked the idea of me working for Cousin Rex. Marriage was my future and father failed to see how pushing around dirty dishes in a plastic trolley would attract the kind of person he wished me to wed. My job Chez Winograd had swollen my father's hump to grotesque proportions. He felt that the only cure was a mate for me to be found among the brens, the ambitious second and third generation boys at the University of Manitoba. Rex's restaurant had become a hangout for a lot of dubious refugees and DPs, displaced persons who had come to Winnipeg after 1945.

My father hated the idea of me associating with "those *tsigayners*, *luftmensch*, and *paskuniaks*." If I mentioned one of them favorably, daddy would ask one question. "Does he speak with an accent?" And if I answered "maybe a little," he would get angry. "Stay away from that *paskuniak*. What do you want with someone who can't speak properly?"

He disliked the tinge of Eastern Europe in anyone's speech except his own. Although he was born in Russia he felt the only good thing about the place was leaving it. The words nostalgia and roots were not part of his vocabulary except when he spoke of his early days in Manitoba, stooking wheat after the First World War. The displaced persons who came after the Second World War reminded him of his own unhappy time. He didn't want his born-in-Canada daughter to be tainted with what he had tried so hard to forget.

Daddy figured if I hung around the library at the University of Manitoba for a couple of years I would certainly attract an accentless hardworking boy. I took the required first year courses, including Rabbi Ripp's. There were only ten people in the class including Norma Bled, Kenny, and Heather Duncan who was a year ahead of me and had to repeat some courses. Heather had been last year's Freshie Queen and her social duties prevented her from studying for exams.

To be a Freshie Queen entailed a lot of activity and no one expected Heather to get good marks. Each faculty chose the prettiest and most well-adjusted first-year girl as their Princess. The newspapers published pictures of all the princesses and described the floats in the Freshie Parade on the front page. There were a series of dances and teas and a grand finale at the civic auditorium, where the Queen was finally selected. Any girl who had been princess was not expected to do well in her year. Although I had not been chosen Freshie Queen or even Faculty Princess, I still failed two of my mid-term exams and received something called 50R for re-read on my essay for Rabbi Ripp.

My only excuse was that I was one of the girls who had to cheer and walk beside the borrowed convertible carrying my faculty's Freshie Princess. The fourth-year boys who organized the event liked to surround the princesses with girls who had been left out, to prove we were loyal and not envious of our candidate for Queen.

If Ronnie had presented my father with two failures and a 50R, he would have slapped my brother's face with his leather slipper. But when I showed him my marks, Daddy only smiled.

"I guess you're no bluestocking, Verna. Just as well. Men don't like going out with girls like your friend Norma Bled who always gets As. The important thing is to have a good time. Go to dances. Even if you aren't a Freshie Princess, you still can go to the dances."

My father realized that someone had to ask me to the parties. He knew college girls could not go by themselves and stand around in clumps as in high school. He understood that I had to wait for my phone to ring. But he didn't have to worry. As soon as I walked into the library the first week at University, I found someone who would take me to any party I wanted. He was a fourth generation, a rich boy, with beautiful diction, who always got As in his exams. Harvey Stone had returned from Massachusetts and had become my companion once again.

Harvey had come fifth in a class of 300 at MIT but the effort had given him shingles. His asthma had been so aggravated that he carried a paper bag in Boston at all times because the humid climate blowing in from the coast made him hyperventilate. Harvey required a dry cold air to survive physically and apparently emotionally as well. Winnipeg provided the physical climate and I provided the emotional one. Harvey was in love with me but I was less than lukewarm. I thought there must be something wrong with Harvey because he got himself in such a frenzy over me. My coldness was due in part to my inferiority complex, my IC. Harvey loved me: something was wrong with Harvey.

Harvey lived in the south end of town, many miles from my house and went to university in the afternoon; the older students had their classes scheduled so they could sleep in. I had to get up at six o'clock three times a week to make an eight o'clock class. On those days, I used to walk a half a mile down Machray Street in the dark morning to catch the streetcar. I always saw the same shadow in the dimness, receding as I came closer, but unmistakable nevertheless. I knew it was Harvey hiding under the scrawny branches of a lilac bush, hoping I wouldn't notice that he had come all the way from the south end, just to watch me take the streetcar to school. My heart turned to acid when I saw the fuzzy silhouette; and by the time I reached university, I was in such a foul mood that I could barely concentrate on taking notes. Harvey would appear by my side, legally, in the library, during the afternoons and joined the Carols, the Normas and the rest in our whispered chats. I never let on that I was aware of his irritating vigil, and he convinced himself that the light was not strong enough in the mornings for me to be aware of his presence.

All the girls felt sorry for Harvey and urged me to accept his invitations.

"At least you go out, Verna, and get to see people. You don't have to be in love with the guy to date him. And maybe you'll meet someone else at the party. You'll never meet anyone sitting at home."

Daddy couldn't see why I didn't wrap the whole business up and become engaged, like Popular Carol. He liked Harvey and thought it charming that his daughter had a lovesick swain.

When Harvey and I went out I hardly talked to him during the evening and always pulled my head away when he tried to kiss me goodnight. I felt nauseated when he came close and imagined that he had a distinctive odor that was seeping into my woolen dress.

Harvey complained of my coldness to Ronnie, Kusy, and Kenny. Kusy and my brother said that I was responsible for Harvey's health and would prove my worth beyond the price of rubies if I declared myself Harvey's steady. Harvey had gained some stature among the boys because he was now considered a local genius who had shown he was as smart as the best at MIT and chose to return home. The male bonding was tight and there wasn't any boy in my circle who would ask me out because he might be responsible for the list of Harvey's allergies increasing over the limits of his fragile constitution.

I was forced to depend on Harvey, exclusively, if I wished to go to parties and the more I went out with him the meaner I became. If I had more strength of character, I could have refused to go with Harvey at all. I didn't have to accept his invitation for New Year's Eve when he asked me on October 4th. But it was necessary to go out and be seen no matter how degrading the date. It was better than staying at home to listen to my mother say, "I hate to leave you alone, Verna, why don't you come to a movie with Daddy and me?" Mother didn't realize that there was nothing more pathetic than a first-year university daughter sitting at the Capitol Theatre with her parents on a Saturday night.

First- and second-year girls were considered the most desirable of dates by fourth-year frat men, the interns at the hospital, and the older boys who were articling in downtown law offices. If a girl had reached third-year university without finding a steady she was beginning to look like a browning fruit. Those girls who had not been plucked out of school for marriage by fourth year never went out, except with their parents to movies in the middle of the week. When the Carols, the Normas and I entered university, we didn't aim for a Bachelor of Arts. As Daddy said, "Just a bachelor is good enough."

The girls who failed to find a husband and graduated were usually sent away (if their parents had money) for further studies in social work.

Once they were out of the city, none of their mothers' friends would remark on their shameful loneliness. Social work was considered appropriate for the BA girls who had become secular nuns. Since they obviously had no looks or personality, God was supposed to compensate the social work girls with overflowing hearts. Norma Shneer who still weighed 200 pounds when she graduated went to Montreal to learn about juvenile delinquents. Mrs. Shneer would say to mother, "Norma wants nothing in life except to help others. Everyone comes to her with their problems." Mother agreed Norma was a saint. She had no other choice. At least I had a choice before I was forced into taking the social work veil. Better to be bad tempered with Harvey Stone than do good works and never go to parties.

Norma Bled was the only girl I knew who actually enjoyed studying. But she was still directing her affections toward Kenny and sat in the hot food cafeteria, where the soup was flavored with saltpeter, talking with him for hours.

I hadn't mentioned Kenny's problem to Norma because I wasn't sure Norma would grasp what I meant. I didn't know what I meant either. I understood that Kenny was not supposed to like fondling girls but I didn't understand exactly what Kenny and Ripp were supposed to do together. No one gave me any anatomical details. What could I say to Norma Bled? Anyway, she'd just think I was making the whole thing up to bring Kenny back my way.

Few of us knew much about things sexual, homo and/or hetero. We had read a book by a doctor and a registered nurse that mentioned wet dreams and erections and had diagrams which might have been in one of Harvey's physics texts. But we thought wet dreams meant bed wetting by adolescents, like one of the unpopular Carols at camp who had to change her sheets every day. We didn't understand why the doctor said only boys had wet dreams. Erection was a mystery. When I was thirteen, my mother gave me a book with a picture of a fox terrier sitting up on his hind legs — full frontal nudity. I noticed that his organ seemed enlarged but I made no connection between the dog and the boys I knew. We girls didn't discuss these things; not out of prudery, but we just didn't have the basics to mull over. We knew how babies came in and out of our own bodies but we were unaware of any of the mechanical complications on the part of the male.

It wouldn't occur to any of us, including Norma Bled, that a boy who didn't kiss too often might be a pansy or a fruit. We would assume that he was shy, or a gentleman who didn't want to get us into trouble. There were a lot of boys who never went further than holding hands and a goodnight kiss after the second date, who eventually married. The faster ones might hold you very close while dancing and dip you backwards during a long beat, placing a leg between yours, ostensibly for support. And sometimes they would kiss a girl publicly on the dance floor. But unless they went steady few girls would allow much more than a nuzzling, neck upwards, in the back seat of a car. And then we'd surreptitiously inspect each others necks for hickeys the following morning.

We did understand one thing, however; the greatest evil that could befall was to be transformed from a mediocre student into an unwed mother. Our pudeur was due to a combination of ignorance and common sense.

We had a terrible example in the year ahead of us, when Heather Duncan was Freshie Queen. Beverlee Kingsley-Peel (daughter of my father's boss) had actually been an unwed mother. She was chosen as a Freshie

Princess, and everyone said that she was the prettiest. But Beverlee disappeared until the following September when Heather Duncan was elected.

The fourth-year boys who controlled the election said that Beverlee had tried to sleep her way to the top. They had cynically used her body and chose Heather instead. Heather, the daughter of an Anglican minister, was elected Freshie Queen, not only for her looks, which weren't as good as Beverlee's, but because she combined a high moral standard with a democratic manner. Heather spoke to everybody and even chatted with Harvey Stone in the library about religion. The lesson was obvious. Heather, who said no, became Freshie Queen and Beverlee, who said yes, was literally scarred for life. One of the Carols saw stretch marks on her stomach in the girl's shower. It was brave of Beverlee to return the following year but none of the boys went near her except for a casual game of hearts in the common room.

I understood that going out with Harvey had advantages. I would never have the same problem as Beverlee; I went to dances, and it tightened my parents' connection even more with Emelia Stone.

Emelia Stone was the aristocratic relation of my Great Aunt and Uncle Miller. Mother was the niece of Great Uncle and Emelia was the cousin of Great Aunt. The Stones were a Winnipeg family who, though once merely nouveau riche, had vastly multiplied their first fortune and become part of the super rich; if they wished they could show their holdings to the Eatons and the Richardsons and still carry their heads high.

When they moved from the Manitoba countryside to Winnipeg it was necessary to get rid of the hayseeds in their pockets by emptying them; they were the largest contributors to charity, from the Jewish national fund to the Salvation Army. The women, drooping with enormous mink coats, used to throw $20 bills over the single dollars in the cut-glass bowls at charitable teas. The more their bank account mounted, however, the more well-bred they became, and the daughters of the loudmouthed free-spending wives began to speak in low voices and wear cloth coats. The second and third generations of those who remained in Winnipeg no longer had any desire to shine philanthropically. They wanted to be loved for their gracious manner and austere habits.

Emelia Stone, the dowager of the family, had initiated this general thriftiness, although, as my father said, "She could buy Poland and still have something left for a few world cruises." Her affairs and functions were always modest; Emelia never did anything showy like hiring caterers or serving whole salmons. Guests were made to feel at home by watching Emelia drying tea cups after dessert, with the help of two or three of her adoring friends — the minnows who always travel in the wake of the big fish.

When Emelia gave a function larger than a dessert luncheon, she borrowed Anka, the devoted maid of my Great Aunt and Uncle Miller, to clean her kitchen.

But when Emelia was asked to other people's affairs, nothing was too good for her. Her friends went so far as to hire Mendel Glow and his staff and order the $6.50 deluxe Tudor dinner, roast haunch of beef, carved in front of you, with Yorkshire pudding (made with extra eggs).

"You'd think she was the Princess of Pinsk, the way people kowtow to her," Zora (no sycophant) would mutter. "They should know better. None of her money is ever going to stick on them."

The Stones and our family would get together at my Great Uncle Miller's once a year on his birthday. The Millers had kind of an open house and people would dribble in during the afternoon. This year, my parents were most anxious that I should go with them because they knew that Emelia would be there. My father wanted to solidify my relationship with Harvey and he thought that a chat between Emelia and Harvey and myself in a familiar setting would be helpful. I went along and slumped beside Harvey, who had accompanied his mother, on Great Uncle's chesterfield.

Emelia Stone had brought a friend, Mrs. Manheim, M. M.'s mother. I sipped gingerale while the two ladies looked me over.

There was no doubt in my mind that Emelia was trying to decide whether I was adequate marriage material for her son. She must have asked Mrs. Manheim to come and help her decide. I felt like an expensive colored refrigerator on Eaton's heavy appliance floor, displaying myself in front of two uncertain shoppers.

"Do you go to school?" Mrs. Manheim asked.

"Of course she goes to school," Emelia replied. "Do you think that her father would let a girl like that sell hairnets at Woolworths?" Emelia didn't know about my former plate scraping job at the House of Norograd.

Mrs. Manheim said, "Do you get good marks at school like my son Martin and," she paused, "Harvey?"

I made a little mincing movement.

"Oh no. I'm not in their league."

Both women looked pleased.

Mrs. Manheim continued. "Girls shouldn't have to worry about doing well at school. As long as they pass. So their father's money won't be completely wasted."

They smiled knowingly.

"I dare say you met Harvey at a dance. You know, I met my husband at a dance. I wouldn't have met and married him if I had stayed home that night to catch up on school work."

I guessed that Mrs. Manheim thought that I was good value for Harvey.

Emelia looked uncomfortable. She felt the conversation was becoming obvious. Emelia didn't think it was nice to say out loud what was on everyone's mind. Mrs.

Manheim must have realized she was going too far and switched the subject to their sons.

She congratulated Harvey on his success at MIT.

"Fifth out of 300 is very good. I hope you do as well as Martin. Of course he went to Harvard and Oxford and came first. You ought to talk to him about your future. He's coming to Winnipeg at the end of this summer."

I was surprised. M. M. had written me that he would be in Spain.

"Why does he want to come back to Winnipeg?" I asked.

Mrs. Manheim looked annoyed. "I see so little of Martin. And all of my friends want to see him too."

Emelia Stone said in her faint voice (one always had to lean forward when she spoke), "Oh! yes, I do hope he comes. I haven't seen him for ages. He must be a very interesting man by now."

I knew that Emelia was making an aspersion on Martin's age. He was twenty-six and most of the men in Winnipeg were married by that time. Harvey had told me that Mrs. Manheim was worried about M. M. and thought he ought to settle down. She didn't like him going to Spain with foreign girls. "I think she wants to pick out a Winnipeg bride."

"That's ludicrous," I replied. "No one picks out brides anymore. I wouldn't let anybody pick out a groom for me. How on earth would a world traveler like M. M. allow his mother to pick out a shallow thing from Winnipeg?"

Harvey looked hurt. He was depending on family matchmaking to lean me in his direction. I wanted to show him that I didn't live in the dark ages.

It was almost a year since I spent that evening with M. M. at Rabbi Ripp's house. He had sent me two postcards with churches on the back from Italy and Spain.

The Italy postcard said, "Three hours in San Vitale at Ravenna. Thirteen hundred years of Byzantium has more to say about death than any memento mori of the Renaissance. Death is the great obsession in my life. Fondly, Martin."

My father read the card. "Any man who spends three hours in a church isn't normal." He shook his head.

The other card came from Leon, in northern Spain.

"I'm going to spend my summer gazing at this plateresque facade. Death is carved in every niche of the cathedral. Fondly, Martin."

Father didn't like it.

"Your cousin Rex is right for once. Too much learning makes a kakapuzti of the brain. Martin Manheim is morbid."

As far as I was concerned, the gloomy impersonality of the messages only increased my belief that M. M. was not a human being but a platonic ideal. The cards might have been sent by the Pope, or T. E. Lawrence or David Ben Gurion. I thought of M. M. as kind of a celebrity pen pal whom I probably would never see face to face. With luck, however, our desultory correspondence might continue for generations. And when M. M. became illustrious in a truly worldwide sense, I could publish the postcards and have a little fame reflect on me.

I was cheered by this thought because all signs in the rest of my life indicated that it was going to be one without interest. I was already on the wide, easy road of mediocrity.

It was the end of my first year of university. I had failed one exam and received a C and three Ds in the rest. Rabbi Ripp said that the beginning sentence of my History of Religion paper had started with a capital letter but none appeared again, nor did any periods, except after the last word in the last page. I wouldn't have minded so much but it seemed my only chance to escape university was to marry Harvey. And I was even beginning to worry that my marks wouldn't be good enough for social work, although they accepted me into second year.

In the meantime, I found a summer job that was supposed to give me some experience in helping others. The municipality appointed me park lady in the East Kildonan. I was supposed to rally the fourteen year olds who frequented Peanut Park into worthwhile activities, to develop their artistic creativity with clay modeling or find an outlet for boisterous behavior in games like Red Rover, Red Rover, Won't You Come Over. I also was supposed to make sure none of the sports equipment was stolen. The first month I chased after the adolescent bikers who liked to take death rides in the wading pool. (The death was meant for any two year old splashing around.)

Halfway through the job, my supervisor told me that more baseball bats had been stolen from my park than six others put together. "And you don't even have the Point Douglas Kids," she remonstrated. My only solution was to lock myself in the sport shack with the equipment when I arrived at 7 a.m. and read the works of Jane Austin until 4:30 when Harvey picked me up.

More important things than summer jobs were in the air, however.

Popular Carol married in early August. Her Harvard man came home and said he could not live without her in Cambridge, Mass. The wedding was catered by Mendel Glow and there was no stinting — fresh whole salmons, shrimp dip in every cranny and a string quartet at lunch. Harvey bought me a wreath of baby orchids to wear like a tiara for the evening dance. When we left that night Harvey took out a Birks box and offered me a pearl necklace as a symbol of our pre-engagement. He didn't believe in fraternities so we couldn't be pinned. If Carol and her frat man could be married, he reasoned, so could we. Harvey explained that our unsettled relationship was making him wheeze like an ill-tuned bagpipe. His doctor told Emelia that asthmatics like Harvey needed routine and stability and there were two institutions that might help. Marriage or the military.

Emelia didn't think Harvey would enjoy soldiering and reluctantly encouraged him to marry. She said she would support him and a wife comfortably while Harvey studied for his Ph.D. anywhere in the world. He even thought he could return to MIT if I went with him.

Although I had trouble making up my mind about most things, I knew I didn't love Harvey. But I still needed an escort, a crutch, and didn't want to be rid of him completely. I just replied, averting my head and standing as far away from him as possible, that "I was far too young to get married," and returned the pearls.

I felt guilty. My father's hump was becoming heavier. I was almost eighteen and was getting too heavy for him to carry around.

11

The Romanoffs of Lancaster Street

I made the mistake of telling my brother, Ronnie, about the gift of pearls. Harvey had become a good friend of his and was helping him build a hi-fi in our basement. My brother thought I was crazy to return the pearls. But Harvey was as scrawny as a chicken with rickets and still had a tendency to talk with his hand cupped over his mouth. He looked a bit more mature than when I first started going with him because his moustache was fuller and the fringe hung well over his upper lip.

Kusy Gwertzman used to come over and watch Ronnie and Harvey work on the hi-fi. Kusy now had a lot of respect for Harvey and no longer mocked him. According to Kusy, Harvey had become a "genuine eccentric." The word genuine was the operative word. If Kusy had merely said "eccentric" in a cynical tone, he would have meant that Harvey was still a fool.

Kusy was the moral leader of the boys in my circle and when he decided that Harvey and his weird ways were acceptable, the normal guys included Harvey in their group. As soon as Harvey became one of the guys, their code of loyalty prevented them from poaching on Harvey's property. Harvey would have had to declare publicly that he was dropping me before one of them would take me around the block for a walk. My feelings never came into question. It would have been unthinkable of me to confide in a friend of Harvey's and tell him I wished to go out with other boys. I would have been considered a Jezebel and risked being stoned in the market place.

Once I went out on a blind date with a boy from Minneapolis who didn't know I was being boycotted in Winnipeg. Kusy waited up for me with Ronnie and when I returned he told me what he thought of my behavior.

"Your sister's a bitch." Kusy spoke for my benefit but directed his words to Ronnie, whom he considered more responsible.

"None of the guys would take her out even if Harvey sent around invitation cards. Everyone thinks she should put Harvey out of his misery and marry him."

Ronnie nodded approval at Kusy's words. Kusy continued.

"Verna, you've got your ass in a tub of butter. Look how rotten you treat Harvey and he keeps coming back for more punishment. What else can a girl like you want? Personally, I think Harvey is nuts, but if that's what he likes it's good enough for me. Be reasonable. Take the pearls." (Ronnie must have told him about the pearls.) "Then take the diamond ring, then have a big wedding and rent a middle-income townhouse in Boston near MIT. Old Lady Stone will pay for everything. Harvey told me so."

Kusy turned to Ronnie. "You ought to tell your father about the pearls. If Verna doesn't get engaged to Harvey quick she'll turn hard and bitter."

Kusy wasn't the only person who was worried about my stalling.

Auntie Zora heard about the pre-engagement offer and their rejection at one of her north end *conversaziones*. Zora always took the gossip at her north end *conversaziones* more seriously than the kind repeated at a south end tea party.

Auntie Zora had a stucco house with a large plot leading to the Red River. She refused to move south because she said south enders were ignorant and pseudo (a favorite word). She would sometimes say, "I need to pluck my share of life's ripe grapes too" and her ripe grapes were her *conversaziones*, on topics like "Milton's Paradise Lost, How Relevant in 1954?" She'd dig up Mr. McKay, my mother's high school teacher, from his potato farm in East Kildonan, to which he had retired a decade before, and use him as group moderator.

Gastronomically speaking, the *conversazione* was classified as a dessert luncheon. When Zora rang my mother and announced, "I'm going to have an intimate function next week," my mother understood that she'd have to start baking for Zora's dessert luncheon. Dessert such as Schaum Torte or Rhum Baba was a certainty along with Melting Moments and Dream cake for nibblers, but there was no rule forbidding a first course of jellied salmon or hot cheese pie.

During one of Zora's *conversaziones*, Ida Bled asked Zora why I was so foolish as to give back Harvey's pearls. I had told Norma about the gift and made her swear secrecy. I suppose Norma didn't think it right to include her mother's ears in the oath. This was the first time Zora realized that Harvey really wanted to marry me.

Ida Bled expressed Zora's thoughts. "Emelia Stone wouldn't give her son money to buy pearls unless she thought they were going to be kept in the family. She wants Verna for a daughter-in-law. She probably picked out the pearls herself. And Emelia in her quiet way likes the best you know. I bet they were natural pearls, not cultured, like my husband bought me from Mickey Moto's in Japan." Mr. Bled had business interests in the orient and Ida was always bragging about her Hong Kong silks and Japanese pearls. But she gave Emelia her due and knew that the Stones could afford better.

Zora looked down on *nouveau riche* types like Ida Bled but she didn't mind the idea of developing closer ties with Emelia Stone. It was definitely better to be equal to Emelia Stone and her blue chip stock and understated tweed suits, than to someone like Kenny's father, the milkman, who didn't even own the dairy.

Zora had continued voicing her suspicions about Kenny's sex life. She figured out that I once had a soft spot for him and felt that it was salutary to keep reminding me that Kenny was a pervert. I wondered if Zora would have harped so much on Kenny's alleged peculiarities if his father owned the dairy. Zora believed that my affection for Kenny showed a dangerous afinity to unsuitable males. Harvey Stone was definitely suitable. Zora decided that I needed a push and she went to my father with the story about the pearls.

"Everyone at the *conversazione* said Verna was crazy to give them back. Sydney, you have to put pressure on that girl. Tell her there's nothing wrong with Harvey Stone."

My father had already been informed about the pearls by Kusy. But when Zora told him that it had become the chief subject, along with Franz Kafka, at her *conversazione*, he knew he had to talk to me. His hump was sore and heavy and even people who he didn't care too much about, Kusy, Ida Bled, and Zora, were trying to show him the way to get rid of it.

"Verna," he pleaded, "what's the matter with Harvey Stone? Look how he helped Ronnie with his hi-fi set. He loves your mother's eggplant salad. You don't know how lucky we all are that a boy like Harvey is interested in you. It won't happen again."

I told father that Harvey was ugly, boring and I hated him coming to the house because I was always stepping over him like a stray cat.

Daddy got angry.

"That's your big trouble. You're so critical. No man likes women who criticize all the time. You criticize me at the dinner table. You even criticize your mother's cooking. And what did that get you? Burning Duck! And now a good boy like Harvey is foolish enough to want to marry you. But he's got something wrong too. A stray cat you call him. You are the cat. Believe me you are going to be a very unhappy girl if you keep finding fault with everything and everybody. Harvey should only know what you are really like. There's no such thing as a perfect man on earth. Someday you'll realize Harvey was your best bet in life."

My father was going to give up the ghost after his little talk with me but Zora had an idea. Great Aunt and Uncle Miller were related to Emelia Stone on Great Aunt's side and had authority in our family. Great Uncle Miller could look dignified on top of a dung heap and Zora thought I might listen to his advice.

My father wasn't so enthusiastic because he had certain reservations about the Millers but he thought it worth a try. He knew that I was a little afraid of Great Uncle Miller.

Until the marriage of their youngest child, Great Aunt and Uncle Miller lived on a respectable street in north Winnipeg. The houses were painted regularly, garbage cans were hidden behind garages uncluttered by debris, and, each year, after the twenty-fourth of May, salvias and pansies were planted in rows.

Then Great Uncle went bankrupt and was forced to move. His new place was on Lancaster Street where boarding houses were indistinguishable from brothels, the road was strewn with empty chip cartons and quack grass and plantain sprouted from the patches of earth in front of decaying clapboard.

But as far as Great Uncle Miller was concerned, he might have been living on Wellington Crescent, Winnipeg's rich man's row. The grass in front of Great Uncle Miller's house reflected a fanatic hatred of anything but the best Kentucky blue. His backyard was a vegetable garden, filled with stacked tomatoes and corn, and a lonely fence, threaded with sweet peas, firmly marked his separation from the rest of Lancaster.

For my father, however, there was nothing more disagreeable than visiting Great Uncle Miller. Apart from wading through the trash, he had to pass by Lila Wees, sitting and staring on her stoop; 170 pounds of fly-specked flesh, every millimetre of her skull barbed-wired with bobby pins. Flies would settle on her and she would never move at all; the insects scattered only when she lifted beer to her lips.

Even worse, when my father visited Lancaster Street he would have to fend off Great Aunt Miller's embrace. When she clutched him, he always turned his face away and yelled, "Get away, get away. I don't need your germs too."

I used to wonder if he believed that living on Lancaster Street increased her microbe count.

Great Aunt Miller always embraced us as if she had just survived a shipwreck — all teary and trembly, even though we saw her every week. "An hysterical," my father called her. "That one can't take a walk without worrying about a sparrow doing something on her head." Anxiety restricted her to such a degree she could do little with purpose or conviction, except put on heavenly blue crepe de chine dresses with white piqué collars and arrange her fine white hair in a soft bun with her Russian filigree combs and argue with Anka.

If a census taker came around and asked what Anka's position was in the household, Great Aunt Miller would have answered, "maid."

But to Great Uncle Miller, Anka was everything that mattered. "The éminence grise, the power behind the throne," Zora said.

Not that she was Great Uncle's mistress, like Edward the VII and Mrs. Keppel. Anka's appearance precluded any hanky-panky. She was younger than Great Aunt, but suffered from some kind of spastic disability or premature physical senility that we children were warned never to mention in her presence. Her thin arms jerked uncontrollably, apparently unconnected to any nerve receiving rational signals from the brain, and she was perpetually stretching her neck while emitting sounds from her throat that had nothing to do with her speech. She wore the same house dress all her life with stockings rolled down to my Great Uncle's discarded bedroom slippers on her feet.

She was not a king's mistress. But she had power all the same.

Anka collected the rents from two houses owned by Great Uncle and scratched out his accounts in a strange kind of Ukrainian cipher that only Great Uncle could make out. She was not really literate, even in Ukrainian, but when she had to mark something down on a paper the dabs looked like $\mathcal{A}$ and $\mathcal{M}$, revealing some training in the Cyrillic alphabet.

Anka was not aware of any tax system in Canada and if Great Uncle Miller felt any obligation of a fiscal nature he never mentioned it to her. She was Keeper of the Purse and even doled out the money to Great Aunt, informing her which week was lean and which was fat, and never hesitated to contradict or quarrel. Her freedom of speech in Great Uncle's house was complete.

When my mother came to visit, Anka, in her frenzied twitching manner, would complain to her about Great Aunt Miller's pathetic attempt at dill pickling, or what a mean thing she said to Great Uncle. Great Aunt, listening almost calmly in her Victorian Lady chair, would finally wave her hand feebly and remonstrate, "Be quiet, be quiet, you get so excited when Fanny comes, what are you doing in the living room anyhow?"

Anka, suddenly struck by her breach of protocol, would back away, like an eighteenth century courtier, into the kitchen, still twitching and complaining, yet acknowledging, by her retreat, Great Aunt's role as the figurehead. She would stay in the kitchen several minutes, listening to my mother and Great Aunt's conversation and then, when something particularly irritating was quavered out by Great Aunt, Anka would rush out again like a boxer from the kitchen corner and batter Great Aunt about.

"Streaky bananas and crusts, dry crusts, that's all she buys when she goes shopping. Mr. Miller will choke to death on those crusts she gives him to eat."

Great Aunt Miller didn't like spending money on food and always bought spotty fruit and kept bread for a very long time. Although she loved her husband, as all wives did at that time in Winnipeg, her great passion in life was frugality. The dry crusts and browning fruit on her husband's plate were not meant personally. Zora maintained, "It's in the family, her sisters are the same way, they've all got the miser germs."

Now Anka would have given Great Uncle Miller all the fingers on her right hand to eat, one by one, if he felt hungry enough.

When she went shopping there would be oranges and even a pomegranate for Great Uncle, as well as the streaky bananas and the stale bread that she and Great Aunt ate.

Great Uncle Miller deserved special treatment.

He was dapper and dignified. He wore spats and a wide panama hat in the summer and there was always a sweet pea in his buttonhole. His conversation was a mixture of talmudic sayings and enticing descriptions of richly veined gold mines in which he wanted everyone, even my father, to invest. My father would as soon throw what little savings he had in the Red River, tied up tight with a pink bow, as buy a share of the mine. But he did admit, "Your Great Uncle is a learned man and knows the Talmud better than anyone else in Winnipeg. At least he can understand what he's reading when he prays, unlike your Uncle Gerald."

This was a great compliment coming from my father who was never impressed by anyone he knew. (In direct contrast to the distaste he felt for his intimates, he regarded any important public figure, like John Diefenbaker, Franklin Delano Roosevelt, and King George as gods. "If it weren't for them we'd all live in caves.")

Great Uncle Miller believed that there was no human action in the world without a talmudic commentary and he spoke in aphoristic terms.

I used to think of him as God's spy, especially when he'd say, "Gold must be hammered and a child must be beaten." Great Uncle never struck a child in his life — he never made the mistake of matching any of his actions to his words.

Great Uncle, with spats and walking sticks and Aunt Miller, with crepe de chine and little veiled hat, could never fit into the Lancaster Street crowd. All contact between them and their neighbors were channeled through Anka. Great Aunt Miller looked straight ahead when she went to buy her cotton piqué ("by the bale," according to Zora) and Anka never allowed Great Uncle to come within a chatting distance of anyone on the street, especially Lila Wees, "the little sloven." Anka accompanied him to the bus every morning carrying his lunch in a paper bag — and every evening at 5 o'clock, when he returned from the bucket shop or wherever he spent his hours, she'd wait at the same stop, to walk him home, growling like a bad tempered Scotch terrier if anyone came near.

Anka's idea of neighborhood diplomacy was a harangue to the death over the wire fence with Lila Wees who used to throw her garbage into the Miller's vegetables. Lila's garbage was usually empty beer bottles and used French safes, which would never break down into any decent kind of compost. Every second year Anka painted the Miller house and all Lancaster would be amused by this unusual and pointless activity.

Every August Anka and Great Uncle Miller would go to the "farm" for several weeks. The "farm" was an unproductive piece of land with potatoes, sour cream from the Holstein (owned outright), and cabbage for their winter menu. Great Aunt, not accustomed to hard farm work, was content to see Anka go with her husband to dig potatoes and crock sauerkraut while she stayed in town near her telephone. There was no prurient speculation whatever about Great Uncle and his housemaid spending a month together alone in some shack southwest of Winnipeg.

What possible impropriety could there be between a gentleman who looked like Romanoff and talked like the Wonder Rabbi of Propoisk, and Anka, the Vibrating Rag Bag?

Now Great Uncle Miller dearly wanted Emelia Stone to buy his farm so that he could invest even more money in his gold mine. When his most precious asset was ordered to go and clean pots and pans at Emelia's, Anka went loaded with the farm's riches: jars of sauerkraut, a bushel basket of new potatoes, and thick yellow cream, crocked, picked and milked by Great Uncle Miller himself. I don't know why he thought rich cream and sauerkraut would stimulate Emelia into a land purchase. Hardly a sensualist, Emelia ate nothing richer than boiled beef and arrowroot biscuits since her husband died fifteen years before.

Although Emelia had no faith in Great Uncle Miller's gold mine and didn't want to buy his land, she visited him frequently and discussed more spiritual matters with him. Zora believed that a face to face confrontation between me and the Stones, with Great Uncle Miller as arbitrator would change my mind. Harvey and Emelia would seem to be a natural part of the Miller environment and become more acceptable to me. But I refused to go to the Millers the same time as the Stones. Mother agreed. She didn't want any embarrassment. My reaction would be unpredictable and she feared that the presence of the Stones might make me say something that she would regret.

When Zora, Ronnie, my parents and I arrived at the Millers, Great Aunt told Anka to serve tea. Anka announced that Great Aunt's honey cake was inedible because it was made three weeks ago.

"She never puts in enough eggs anyhow," Anka told Zora.

While the cake controversy continued, Great Uncle Miller in spats and boutonniere, led me out to the vegetable garden as far away from Lila Wees' house as possible.

He explained to me what a fine thing it was to be a member of the Stone dynasty.

"It's not just marrying Harvey. Although there's nothing wrong with him. But his family has connections all over the world. There are Stones in Paris who live like dukes. You could visit them on your honeymoon. The Stones in England are more intellectual — maybe you'd like them better. One is a scientist, like your father, but he's much richer. He lives in a castle in the middle of London, like the Queen. Emelia stayed there on her last trip to England. If you marry Harvey, all these people will be your relations."

Anka had come into the garden, ostensibly to pick some early peas but really in order to butt into our conversation.

"Even if he asked me today," Anka mused from behind the vines of climbing vegetables, "you wouldn't catch me marrying Harvey Stone."

"He's not asking you," Great Uncle replied. "Are you crazy."

"I'm not crazy. He's crazy. When I go to Mrs. Stone's to clean, all that Harvey does is wash the hands. Every 15 minutes. Comes to my sink and washes the hands, with the sunlight soap. The big yellow bar that I use to scrub the dirty dustcloths. It so strong it makes my hands all red."

She held up her bony red fingers.

"But at least I have no sores on my hands. I don't think it's good that Verna marries someone with sores on his hands."

I always thought the scabs on Harvey's hands were because he scratched his hives. I didn't know he washed his hands every 15 minutes. I thought he went to the bathroom so often because he had a nervous bladder.

Great Uncle questioned Anka.

"Maybe he's tinkering on some dirty wires." He knew that Harvey liked to build things.

Anka shook her head.

"He don't tinker in his bedroom. He just lies on the bed, with his head hanging over where his feet should be and plays records. That's not tinkering. When the record stops he goes to the sink, turns on the tap and scrubs and scrubs with the big yellow soap for 10 minutes. I can't even get to the sink to rinse the clothes. I tell Harvey his hands are full of sores from the soap but he doesn't listen to me. His mother knows too. I hear her cry in her room."

Great Uncle Miller looked away.

"That's enough, Anka. Go inside."

She left us and he paused.

"I think you should wait a bit, Verna. Maybe go out with some other boys in the meantime. You're young, only 18. Harvey will wait for you if he wants. I don't know why your father is pushing you."

"When you marry a daughter a hump is off your back" — a deplorable maxim born in eastern Europe where women ate standing like oxen and were frequently hitched to the traces of a plough.

In Canada, fathers cherish their daughters, send them to university and believe they are just as good as sons. Deplorable ethnic maxims whatever their truth should go back to where they came.

But I had placed just below mediocre in my university exams and been fired from my job as Park Lady. When all was said and done my marriage to Harvey would have given the family a chance to worry about someone else. Zora thought that Great Uncle Miller had been hasty in his judgment but Daddy agreed with him.

"I don't want a son-in-law who's crazy. Craziness can be catchy as scarlet fever. If I let Verna marry Harvey, she'd go for the laundry soap too."

And he warned Ronnie. "If Harvey comes around to the house because of the hi-fi set, keep him in the basement. And watch if he goes to our sink."

It was the end of summer and I had nothing to look forward to except working harder at university and going out less often on Saturday nights. At least with Harvey I never had to sit home.

I felt that only a spider web prevented me from falling into a cesspool. All I wanted was a respectable date who would take me out and make no serious demands. Although Popular Carol had married, I had no desire to follow her example. The fact was I became sour when I didn't go out. This upset my parents and made them think of marriage as a solution. Otherwise, they wouldn't have minded if I hung around a few more years.

It was nine o'clock on a Friday night and I was listening to Ronnie explain what a sigmoidascope examination entailed when the telephone rang. Ronnie answered.

"It's for you," he said, holding the receiver in my direction. "Sounds good. A strange male voice. Talk nicely unless he's an obscene caller."

I said hello as tenderly as I knew how.

"Hi, little duck. Remember me. It's the man who eats green butter. I'm in town for nine days. Are you free tomorrow night?"

I was surprised. I thought M. M. had been swallowed by one of the gargoyles imbedded in the stone facade of one of the plateresque churches. I wondered if I should play it coy. If I accepted, he might think that I was unpopular because I didn't have a date Saturday night. Some girls made it a policy never to accept dates for Saturday night from Wednesday on. They preferred to sit home in secret than have a boy know they weren't booked at least three days in advance.

"Saturday night," I said aloud, in a dubious tone.

Ronnie was eagerly listening.

"Say yes, fool, yes. If you don't, I'll tell you how a proctologist spends his working hours."

I wanted to say yes and Ronnie had given me moral support.

My family seemed pleased that M. M. had asked me out. Ronnie did say that he thought M. M. was too old for me. But mother declared our age distance negligible.

"Gerald is ten years older than Zora and look what a

happy marriage they have. Martin Manheim is only nine years older than Verna. I know of course," mother hastily added, giving me a fearful look, "Verna is not interested in marriage. It's just a date. I'm just happy you're going out, for your sake, that's all. You get so crabby when you sit around the house."

I said, "Don't get so excited about M. M. He's leaving in nine days."

Mother didn't reply but I understood that M. M.'s call had given her fresh hope, at least for a better tempered daughter.

M. M. rang the door bell earlier than expected. Mother answered and spoke in what I thought to be a mannered Lady Teazle tone.

"How do you do Mr. Manheim. Back from Oxford I see. Come and meet my husband and Verna's father."

Irritating. Mother had never called Kenny, Harvey, or Kusy "Mister." It was as if M. M. was an old man, a contemporary of my father, or even worse, of Mr. Kingsley-Peel, his boss. Why should M. M. talk to Daddy anyhow? I was always embarrassed when an intellectual had to engage Daddy in conversation. Daddy didn't believe in dialogue, just declaration. He stated what was on his mind and was indifferent to response.

But Daddy rose from his chair, greeted M. M. at the door and shook his hand as if Prince Philip had just dropped in from England.

He had never shaken Harvey's hand.

My parents were trying to ingratiate themselves with M. M. Was it because Mrs. Manheim was the next best thing to Emelia Stone? Or was it because M. M. was a famous don? Daddy evidently had forgotten about the death postcards. Or at least he didn't believe that thinking on mortality was as bad as washing hands every fifteen minutes.

I managed to pull M. M. out of the house after Daddy

gave his opinion of Englishmen. "Englishmen are polite. But a lot of them look like sissies."

Although M. M. was born a Winnipegger, father must have thought he had changed into an Englishman because of the yellow tweed suit and the umbrella. Especially the umbrella. In Manitoba, it usually rained too hard for umbrellas to be of any use. Or it didn't rain at all. Only ladies who had just been to the beauty parlor worried about a few drops of moisture on their heads.

M. M. started up his car and announced, "This might be a bore but I couldn't think what else to do. I made a reservation at Pierre's restaurant for an early dinner. That should give us enough time afterwards to go for a walk in the rain, at a cemetery."

I was overwhelmed by the casual way M. M. mentioned Pierre's, the most expensive restaurant in town, and uneasy about the cemetery walk. My emotions were mixed but I concentrated on the positive.

None of the boys I knew, including Harvey, had sufficient funds or poise to take a date to Pierre's. It was Popular Carol who had told us about the popovers — I had never sampled them myself. She had gone there with her Harvard fiancé two days before her wedding — as a kind of preview of married life. Popular Carol's marriage definitely included meals at expensive restaurants with at least two servings of popovers, the first before the soup, and the second during the main course, accompanied each time by unsalted butter.

I wondered if M. M. might not be aware of the prices at Pierre's. "Never take a man for a ride," Daddy had warned. "A smart man smells out the golddiggers."

"Pierre's will cost you a lot of money."

M. M. appeared amused.

"If I have taken Gwen to the Savoy Grill in London, Sybil to Lapérouse in Paris, and Harriet to Lockobers in Boston, I can manage taking Verna to Pierre's in Winnipeg. It is also my habit, wherever in the world, to stroll among some tombstones after the meal, preferably in the rain. If we do that, you and I can tell each other our greatest fears."

The walk part bothered me and I said that it wasn't going to rain, hoping that would make him drop the whole idea.

"Of course it's going to rain. When I carry an umbrella there's always a bit of a drizzle."

I couldn't help but be impressed by his confidence. But I didn't want to tell him my greatest fears. I wasn't sure what they were. Leaving home? Staying home and being the spinster daughter? Going to the proctologist? Such things could not be discussed with a sophisticate like M. M. who was the opposite of Harvey. Sure of himself. Hands clear of scabs. (Maybe that's why Daddy shook hands with him.) As we drove up to the restaurant, he discussed what he liked to eat.

"My favorite food is white asparagus which you eat with the fingers. After the meat course, before the dessert. Mind you there are certain things I would never touch. Pineapple gives me heartburn and I'd never trust an oyster. But I eat everything else. Even the pork pies served in college, which invariably have a dead fly cooked underneath the crust. The English," he explained, "are not very clean. I should tell your father that they never wipe the restaurant tables."

Pierre's was not only clean, it had paintings in gold frames of bewigged French kings, and a candle and fresh carnations on the real tablecloths. A man dressed like the Count of Monte Cristo placed a menu in front of me, heavily embossed with gold lettering and with shaggily cut edges, like Popular Carol's wedding invitation.

I was intimidated by the words, "harengs en crème," "chateaubriand," and the rest of the people in the restaurant who were well over 30.

The count bent over me and asked, "What will Mademoiselle have?"

I was numb. I didn't know whether to order one, two, or three courses; to order them all at once, or one at a time.

Even more important, I was terrified that I would choose something too expensive. I searched the prices until I found the lowest number and asked for the dish it corresponded to by pointing.

The Count said loudly, "You want potato soup Miss?"

I nodded. He looked doubtful but wrote it down, and continued to stand there, his pencil poised. After a while he spoke.

"And after potato soup?"

I looked at M. M. for help but he was studying his menu and not paying attention. I chose the next lowest price on the menu.

"Omelette please."

"Omelette?" The count's eyebrows rose. "What kind of omelette?"

The menu didn't specify the kinds of omelette or if there was a difference in price between them. I was afraid if I ordered a mushroom or a ham omelette it might cost extra.

"Plain omelette," I whispered.

He had an edge in his voice when he asked, "Salad?"

"No thank you."

"Peas?"

"No thank you."

"Fried potatoes?"

I knew potatoes had to be cheap. At the House of Norograd Lord Rex threw in the potatoes for nothing.

"Yes, please."

The waiter left my side and walked over to Martin. M. M. looked up and said firmly, "I will begin with lobster cocktail. And then bring me a filet mignon, rare. If it is not rare, it will be sent back to the kitchen. Salad please, with vinegar and olive oil. And mushrooms on the side but no potatoes. I shall decide on dessert afterwards."

After the waiter left, M. M. said, "You're the first girl I have taken out who ever ordered fried potatoes. Don't you worry about putting on weight?"

"I asked for fried potatoes," I said, my heart brimming with envy over his filet and lobster, "because my mother always told me to order the cheapest thing on the menu."

M. M. thought this was funny.

"Why didn't you ask the chef to beat you an omelette from one egg only? That might have saved me at least a quarter."

I must have looked unhappy. "I'll tell you what," he said. "You can have a taste of all of my food. And make sure you order the most expensive things on the menu when I bring you back tomorrow night.

"Still, you're not as bad as Dundee Weintraub. I went to Spain with her and she only ate raw vegetables. Dundee would buy a bunch of carrots in the market and scrape them clean at the hotel restaurant. She even asked for an extra plate and knife. The waiters detested her."

It was nice that M. M. thought I was a better companion than Dundee. And our walk in the cemetery wasn't as bad as I feared since neither Kusy Gwertzman, Norma Shneer or anyone else was around to spread the word about M. M.'s unusual interests.

He picked me up every morning at 11, the tombstone tours already written out in a fine leather notebook purchased in Cadiz. Sometimes he went to St. John's Anglican Cemetery, one of the oldest in Manitoba, with many pathetic inscriptions because of the young deaths. "Of every tear that sorrowing mortals shed on such green graves some good is born, some gentler nature comes."

When I pointed out Charles Dickens' optimistic words written on one of the stones, M. M. was not cheered. He felt certain that he was slated and received no comfort from the idea that his early death would at least augment the virtues of his mourners. In the Jewish cemetery early deaths were represented by a facsimile of half a tree, a symbol for being cut down in the middle of life.

"I'll probably have one of my own in a few years time." M. M. stared gloomily at the granite stump.

When I looked uneasy or bored if he went on too long with such speculations, M. M. suggested popovers at Pierre's for our evening meal, to perk me up. He had a deft way of combining the spiritual with the material that appealed to me very much.

"I love to watch you eat," he used to say. "You enjoy food more than anyone else I know, except Sir Maurice Bowra, the Warden of Wadham College. Sir Maurice has no neck, and I can still see yours."

M. M. talked a lot about eating but I was the one who went in for action. The nice thing about M. M. was that he didn't make me feel guilty about being a glutton. He offered me snacks every hour.

"How about some Kelekis chips?" he'd say, passing a well-known take-out stand.

"Let's drive twenty miles to Lockport. Skinners of Lockport puts onions in their hot dogs. You might like that."

Occasionally we would go to Eaton's third floor counter and he would urge me to order a clubhouse sandwich and chocolate cream pie even though he just wanted tea with lemon.

"I just ate breakfast an hour ago. You go ahead. You're still growing."

Surprisingly I didn't put on weight. My stomach was perpetually in movement, churning, tensing, burbling with nervousness. My gastrointestinal system was practicing for some kind of digestive Olympics, energizing enzymes, sending the gastric fluids on a high jump that reached my throat. I needed all the calories I could get. I was exhausted from trying to keep up a worldly banter appropriate to my company.

For the first time in their lives, my parents went on a vacation to visit the chafing dish relations in California. I had inherited my mother's guilt about unreturned hospitality and wanted to pay M. M. back for his restaurant and snack bar treats. I asked him for dinner the day before he was to return to England.

I would never have invited M. M. if my parents had been at home. The only boy I knew who had eaten dinner with his girl's parents was Popular Carol's Harvard man, just before they announced their engagement. Even Harvey had never eaten dinner with my family, just late evening tea. With my parents away, I could ask M. M. without him thinking that he was being snared. I told Ronnie he could join us, not that I wanted him, but I knew he had a right to share the food. Ronnie said that he would be late at the hospital and might come in afterwards.

I set the dining table with the Aynsley, but the chicken hadn't been broiled enough and blood oozed out when M. M. cut off a wing.

"I can't eat this, Verna. Let's try dessert."

I had made lemon tarts and the crust was as hard as the granite tombstones we had visited. I wasn't surprised when M. M. scooped out the filling, leaving the empty shell. "You don't mind if I just eat the gooey part?" he said.

After dinner we went into the living room and M. M. put on his favorite record (he had brought it with him), Beethoven's violin concerto. I was silent, pretending to listen but wondering if M. M. was hungry. Then M. M. spoke. His words startled me more than any others I heard so far in my life.

"How about having coffee with my mother in the Georgian Room at the Bay? When I am gone."

It was not customary for the girls I knew to meet their dates' mothers at downtown department stores. The only time I met Emelia Stone was at Great Uncle Miller's. Even then it was not a tete-a-tete. Mrs. Manheim obviously thought she had the right to give me a once over and I resented the idea. After all I was hardly M. M.'s fiancée. This was 1955 and M. M. was a connoisseur, a don, and old enough to look after himself. He should have detached himself long ago from his mother's influence.

"I will not meet your mother for coffee. Did Dundee Weintraub meet your mother at the Georgian Room and scrape her carrots there?"

M. M. was unsure of himself.

"She just wants to know you a little better."

"What for? I'm not going out with your mother."

I felt dominant for the first time in our relationship.

"Well," he answered slowly. "She knows I have been seeing a lot of you. She thought it would be friendly if you were to meet her as well as me."

"I've only gone out with you for nine days, including last year. Many men have taken me out longer than that, and never have asked me to meet their mothers." Exaggeration about my popularity wouldn't harm.

M. M. sat there quietly, until the record needle began to scratch. He lifted it off.

"This is different. She thinks you might become her daughter-in-law."

My jaw dropped. A red-breasted grosbeak could have flown in without choking me.

Just before the words, "daughter-in-law," I heard Ronnie slam the front door, returning from the hospital. He had a hard day looking up and down either ends of people, and walked into the room eating a banana, sat down beside M. M., nodded politely, and picked up the funnies. I ignored Ronnie. He had a right to read the funnies in his parents' living room.

"What do you mean daughter-in-law?" I repeated.

M. M. was disconcerted by Ronnie sprawled on the love seat, well into L'il Abner. But he pushed on.

"I told my mother that it wasn't entirely impossible, maybe in a couple of years, especially if neither of us finds anyone better, and if you like the notion, we might marry."

Ronnie put down the funnies and said, "I'm going upstairs. If you need me Verna, just yell."

He gave Martin a long, cold medical stare — there was a chance M. M. might be psychotic.

The telephone rang. It was my parents in California wondering if their children were alive and the house still stood after three days of absence.

Ronnie lifted the receiver and heard his mother's voice. In response to "Is everything all right?" he said, "I don't know. Martin Manheim is here and wants to marry Verna. You better come home."

My father, being hard of hearing, often misinterpreted conversations, especially long distance telephone ones. He would hear a name, a phase, and make up the rest of the story himself.

Years before, second cousin Florence called Winnipeg, just to say hello from Detroit, and remarked that her husband Harry was in bed with flu. My father believed long distance calls only happen in the case of calamity or great good fortune. He said to Florence, "That's too bad, I don't think we can come to the funeral," and hung up because he didn't want to cost her a lot of money. He told mother, "There's a terrible bug in Illinois. It'll come up here in a couple weeks. Don't let the children go to any public places. Florence's Harry died of it."

Florence was mother's relation so she commandeered the rest of the Winnipeg relatives into sending a telegram.

"Our hearts are with you at this sad time. Think of

the happy years you had with Harry. You have lost the best."

They signed the telegram with the names of wives, husbands, and children separately, to show that each member of the family, even the two year olds, were truly in sympathy. There were forty-seven names on the telegram and Florence told mother afterwards that Harry nearly had a double pneumonia when he read it.

Mother had called from California but she made the mistake of repeating the words, "Marry Martin Manheim?" in front of father. He immediately assumed this was a great good fortune phone call, grabbed the receiver and asked for Martin, who by this time thought that he had been set up by my family.

My father yelled into his ear, "Congratulations. You'll never have to be ashamed of Verna. And we'll have a wedding even your mother will like." (Martin's mother was fussy, being more social than mine.) "But remember, a marriage to my daughter has to last all your life."

And he hung up. He thought he had got rid of his hump.

Martin stared at me, unhappily.

"Does this mean you'll meet my mother at the Georgian Room?"

I hadn't liked the way everybody swept my decision away from me. I was angry at my father for assuming I had accepted, and not even wanting to speak to me. He had mixed everything up. It was Ronnie's fault.

M. M. argued. "I didn't really mean marriage now. I just wanted you to consider the idea. Take your time.

"Go out with others. I'll do the same. Maybe in a few years time, when you're twenty-one, you'll know what you want."

I sensed that M. M. was relieved by my doubt. He had not really planned to ask me to marry him.

In fact he said, "Never mind about meeting my

mother in the Georgian Room. It was a stupid idea. You're not really ready for anything like that."

We agreed to drop the thought of marriage.

M. M. left for England the next day. But he must have mentioned the incident to his mother before he left, including the telephone call from California.

13
Flora's Arrangements

Amid all the emotions I was prey to after M. M. left, surprise was one of the strongest. I couldn't understand why an intellectual sophisticate, who took out Dundee in Spain, Gwenneth in England and Harriet in Boston, had thought marriage to an unschooled eighteen-year-old over-eater to be a constructive move in his life. Was I overestimating M. M.'s qualities? Perhaps there was a fraudulence in his character that I had been unable to detect because of my youth and naivité.

It was understandable for me to have a small town north end way of looking at the world. I could barely imagine life beyond Machray. But M. M. had to be different; he had left the south end years ago. It never occurred to me that M. M.'s parents still played a heavy role in his life or that he would listen when they told him who to marry.

I was wrong.

Mr. and Mrs. Manheim, though showing pride to the world over their son's scholastic success, were anxious and wanted him home. Mr. Manheim, like my father, hated the yellow suit and feared that Oxford was changing his son into an alien fop. Flora Manheim was afraid Martin might marry a foreign girl who would take him away from her forever. The Manheims, despite their high tone, south end address, had north end views. Daddy often pointed out that Mrs. Manheim was born upstairs on Magnus Avenue not far from the wrongie section in the north end.

Frank Manheim's parents had emigrated from Russia in the late nineteenth century and he was born in Selkirk, a small town near Winnipeg. Typically, he felt it was madness for a son to wander when his parents had already found a faultless world in Winnipeg with the best kind of girls — anchored to their homes, better looking and less aggressive than the Toronto and New York *cholerias*, so vulgar and mouthy. God knows what English girls were like, except they had thick ankles. Winnipeg's daughters would learn to put up dill pickles after marriage and knew the meaning of a clean house. Above all, they cared about their families and visited the parents from both sides with their new husbands, twice a week, alternating Friday night and Sunday lunch.

The Manheims were sure that if M. M. married a local girl she would force him to abandon the misogynist cloisters of Oxford. Women were forbidden to eat at High Table. Mrs. Manheim had seen how it was when she visited Martin. No sensible Winnipeg goddess would settle for eating sardines out of a can in an unheated flat while her husband trotted off several times a week to dine with the rest of the dons on grouse and Rhum Baba.

M. M.'s short visit had been their last chance to bring him back to the real place, his roots and to themselves.

The Manheims had traveled all over the world — but Venice, Tangiers, Honolulu compared unfavorably to Winnipeg. Mrs. Manheim, when told of a local custom, would comment, "That's queer. In Winnipeg we eat at seven." Or, "No one at home uses place mats, not even Emelia Stone."

The finest standards were set by Winnipeggers and the Manheims traveled, in part, to see if the rest of the world measured up.

Mrs. Manheim was aware that Emelia Stone had wanted her Harvey to marry me. If I was good enough for the aristocracy, I would do for Martin.

During his visits, Mrs. Manheim campaigned for me as daughter-in-law while M. M. ate his breakfasts. I had no idea I was running.

The Manheims knew little of my parents except one thing. Mr. Manheim was president of a benevolent organization which collected money for old folks homes, burial societies and free loans to bankrupts and people who had other difficulties, like Tsippe Persky, the beadle's daughter who had a withered arm from polio.

If moral worth, in my parents' mind, was connected to the flakiness of the wife's pie crust, Mr. Manheim had his own rule for judging people. Every year his charity published a book containing the list of those who pledged money and the amount in one column, and their actual contribution in another. Mr. Manheim looked up my father's name and was impressed with his donation, knowing that rich men contributed less.

He instructed his son. "You won't go wrong if you marry the little girl. She comes from a good family."

M. M., disoriented because of his long absence from Winnipeg, took their advice more seriously than he would have if he had been alone in Oxford. Besides, I had laughed at his jokes and didn't scrape carrots in public places. He could see no overwhelming flaw, except my youth — which in a way was an advantage. Although M. M. still allowed his parents an authoritative role in his life, he disliked anyone besides them telling him what to do. An older girl might have been headstrong and quarreled with his decisions. But I showed little initiative and seemed happy when he planned my day.

One of the reasons I disliked Harvey was because he kept asking me where we should go. I believed Harvey ought to have made the decisions and then I would have fallen in with his wishes, reserving the right to complain if I did not have a good time.

My favorite heroes were Mr. Rochester in *Jane Eyre* and Mr. D'Arcy in *Pride and Prejudice* — strong willed older men who were always Mister to their women. Such men, although they treated their lovers with firmness and humorous condescension, could be counted on never to betray.

I needed direction in my life and could not find it within myself. My weaknesses, IC, and disorganization, matched well with M. M.'s nature, his confidence and need to impose intelligent order upon chaotic situations and people.

M. M. liked to control and I was content to be directed. The submissive side of my character and M. M.'s dominating approach, combined with the hopes of our families, had pushed M. M. over the edge to marriage.

And now he was sorry.

A week had passed since M. M. had left and he sent me a letter saying that he was afraid he had frightened me with his "suggestion" (he didn't put the word "proposal" on paper) and again confirmed our decision to drop the matter. That's how things stood between M. M. and myself.

But it was a different story with the parents.

Mine had cut their trip short following the phone call and returned after three days in California. When my father came in the front door with the suitcases he assumed I was engaged. He kissed me with great ceremony, his face alight with congratulations.

"It's off," I said brutally. "I can't marry Martin. We've known each other exactly nine days."

I knew this was an anti-climax for my parents and wished with all my heart they had finished out their time in California — their first holiday in twenty-two years.

Daddy was furious. "What's wrong with Martin Manheim? Why do you have to know him more? He has a law degree and comes from a good family. I know you Verna. You can't decide anything. That's your big problem. Believe me you're making a mistake. Write him and say that you have changed your mind."

Mother disagreed.

"If Verna doesn't want to marry Martin Manheim that is her prerogative. I just want her to do what she wants. Don't listen to your father."

Mother's words made me even more uneasy than father's. The fact was I didn't know what I wanted. I had refused M. M. more from shock at the unexpectedness of his "suggestion" than anything else.

I was conservative and the idea of any change was upsetting. Yet I wanted to leave home and was afraid to go by myself. Perhaps it would be a good idea to marry M. M. and visit Europe — much better than going alone.

The only person I had ever fallen in love with was Kenny and I had written him off because of sexual confusion. But there was something else about Kenny that bothered me. His silences made me fidgety. I liked conversation and M. M. was the only man I knew who talked a lot without becoming a bore. But I had turned him down and M. M. was obviously relieved. I was more in a turmoil than ever. Was Daddy right? Had I made the worst mistake in my life?

It was early autumn and I was attending my second year of University. Attending but not paying attention. All I could think about was M. M.'s "suggestion" and had stopped taking notes in Political Science I and History of Religion II.

Now Zora and mother had a new topic — the Manheim family. I listened, fascinated, as they discussed Mrs. Manheim.

Auntie Zora had never spoken well of Mrs. Manheim because of certain fund-raising feuds. During the war, Zora and Mrs. Manheim had been on an executive committee for raising War Bonds and Zora was bitter because Mrs. Manheim, she said, had hogged everything to herself. But now Zora began to see her virtues.

"When Flora Manheim ran that War Bond Drive she really put my back up. Not only mine, Emelia Stone was furious too. We didn't speak to her for months. But you have to hand it to Flora, although it kills me to say it. She raised more money than anyone else."

Zora looked at mother significantly.

"Leave it to Flora. She gets what she wants. She always has. Lucky she has Frank Manheim for a husband. Everyone says he has a wonderful nature, even though he looks sloppy in those cheap suits. You know, the kind that sell for $49.99 at The Man With The Axe, with two pairs of pants. Even Sydney wouldn't wear those suits."

Zora turned to me.

"Martin probably takes after his father, except for the clothes."

M. M. had told his parents everything, including how my parents jumped the gun during the California phone call. He had stated firmly, however, that I had rejected his proposal. He had done what his parents had wanted and felt relieved of any more filial duty. As soon as he reached England, he called up Gwenneth, the daughter of a Labour peer, and asked her to a concert at Albert Hall.

But Mrs. Manheim believed that my parents' ecstatic reaction on the telephone was far more important than any shilly-shallying on the part of a malleable eighteen year old. She looked upon her son's engagement to a Winnipeg girl as a *fait accompli*. It was just a matter of arranging details.

About three weeks after Martin's departure and two precise letters from M. M., one to me and one to his mother, each giving his view that marriage between us was off, Mrs. Manheim called my mother. Neither of us knew about the other's letter.

"I have heard so much about your daughter from Martin. He thinks Verna's most unusual, with such a sense of humor too. And I have always wanted to get to know you better, Fanny. Emelia Stone says you're like a ray of sunshine. Why don't you and your husband and the children come to our house for a glass of sherry on Rosh Hashanah. We can drink to the New Year together.

Mother was flattered and accepted immediately. I dragged my feet. I assumed Mrs. Manheim was having a big party.

"If you want to get friendly with Mrs. Manheim, you don't need me. It's just for old people anyhow."

But Mother insisted.

"You're a big girl now, Verna. If someone invites you to a grown up party, you have to go. Besides, Mrs. Manheim has some beautiful things in her house and it will be a chance to see them."

My father, who ordinarily hated going to strangers' houses, admonished me.

"Be polite, Verna. In this life you have to be sociable." He turned to mother, "Buy Verna a dress from Holt Renfrew."

The New Year was early that September and the sun was still shining when we drove up to the Manheim home. Mrs. Manheim had asked us for five o'clock specifically, before the setting of the sun. "Don't be late," she told mother. "Five on the dot."

I didn't see any other cars parked in front and I was worried that I was overdressed in my new red velvet, as well as overheated.

"It's going to be just us," I said to mother. "I could have worn a blouse and skirt."

"You look just fine," she said. "Maybe we are the first."

Mr. Manheim, smiling, opened the door before we had a chance to ring.

Mrs. Manheim greeted us in the hall, a dignified-looking blonde lady, with an old-fashioned hourglass figure, wearing a muted green dress made up in a soft rich-looking fabric. Zora had told me to note her clothes. "I say this about Flora Manheim. She knows how to dress. Not flashy. But everything she has looks good. Her small waist helps, of course."

The Manheims oozed out their welcome. Mrs. Manheim brushed a few specks off Daddy's hat as she put it away in the closet and Mr. Manheim looked me up and down and said red was his favorite color. Daddy liked this kind of reception and warmed up enough to compliment Mrs. Manheim on the knickknacks, the Meissen, the Venetian glass, and two elaborately chased silver wall plaques blinding us with roseate flickerings, reflections of the reddening sun.

There was no one else in the living room and I stared through the swagged gold curtains, wondering if others would be driving up soon.

Mr. Manheim said, "Let me get you something to drink," and rolled up a tea wagon with crystal decanters and with sherry, rye, and ice in a silver bucket with matching tongs.

Mrs. Manheim sighed. "It would be wonderful if we really had a special something to drink to, aside from just the New Year. Then I'd bring out champagne."

The telephone rang from another room. Mrs. Manheim disappeared and we stood, glasses in midair, not knowing whether to wait for her to return because Mr. Manheim had begun a toast to "Fanny's smile."

None of us realized, except Mrs. Manheim, that it was Martin calling from Oxford, to wish his parents a Happy New Year. Mrs. Manheim had written him to call precisely at this time, knowing I would be in the house. She, of course, hadn't told M. M. that I was going to be present. M. M. had been steadily taking out Gwenneth, the Peer's daughter, since their Albert Hall date. I was the last thing on his mind.

The telephone was in what the Manheim's called the

library and we could hear Mrs. Manheim's voice through the open door.

"Martin, guess who's here? Verna. She's come with her parents. We're just in the middle of toasting your future life together. Verna has changed her mind. Now I know you'll want to speak to her yourself and tell her how happy you are. Her parents are here and they expect it. Verna's dying to speak to you."

She put down the receiver and ran to call me. M. M. was in shock. But like Mr. Rochester and Mr. D'Arcy, M. M. was a man of his word. He had committed himself once, in front of my family (Ronnie) and he knew what he had to do.

Mrs. Manheim said, "Hurry up, Verna. He's calling long distance all the way from Oxford only because I told him you would be here."

Then covering the speaker she commented, "Now reconsider your decision. It would make everyone so happy."

I knew I was being grossly manipulated but I didn't care. The Manheim's and my parents crowded around as I picked up the phone. The connection from England was poor and I thought I heard M. M. say querulously, "Is that you Verna? Have you changed your mind?"

Mrs. Manheim was explaining the situation to my confused parents. "He's asking Verna to marry him. Martin's crazy about her. Say yes, Verna."

She held up her glass. My father gestured a bottoms up sign. Mother was pink and silent. Three voices kept repeating, "Say yes, say yes, say yes."

I loved being the center of such attention. So much power to make everyone glad. I was scarcely aware of M. M. on the other end of the line.

I yelled into the phone. "Yes Martin, I'll marry you."

A shout went up around me. Mother had tears in her eyes.

M. M.'s voice, barely audible, bleated, "OK, Verna, whatever you want."

Mrs. Manheim grabbed the receiver and congratulated Martin. Then Mr. Manheim did the same and finally my parents.

Mrs. Manheim said, "Goodbye, Martin. I'll write to you when to come home for the wedding," and hung up.

I had such a sensation of joy. At least something was happening to me that everybody said was good. After we drank a toast to me in champagne, Mrs. Manheim's executive quality pierced through our euphoria and she asked for a policy decision.

"I suppose the wedding will be in the spring, so Verna can finish her year?"

That's just what I didn't want. I hadn't been taking notes and I knew I would fail my Christmas exams. I could never concentrate on catching up now that I was engaged and certainly would brood about my decision the longer the wedding was put off.

Like Lady MacBeth, I believed, "If it were done when 'tis done, then twere well it were done quickly."

"It has to be December," I said, not giving further explanation.

Mrs. Manheim poured second glasses of champagne and we drank to a Christmas wedding.

14
The Princess
of Pinsk

The weeks before the wedding were some of the happiest in my life. I did not have to go to university and take notes, apply for typing jobs or flatter oafish boys so I would have a date Saturday night. I didn't even have to be nice to Martin since he was far away.

I was the Princess of Pinsk at the luncheon given in my honor at the Royal Alexandra Hotel. Jealous perfumed ladies, whose daughters were still fretting over Iago's motivations in Arts II and writing term essays on "Whither India," cooed over my peau de soie dress.

Nothing was too good for me. We drove to Minneapolis, eight hours away, to buy my wedding gown. The dresses were kept in a secret room at the back of the store and we sat in a drawing room on velvet chairs the color of eggshells while a duchess brought forth gowns, one by one, spreading out their skirts like fans. There was perked coffee in Doulton cups and dark chocolate to nibble on in a crystal dish. A seamstress stood by, on call, to take in and let out and the white telephones kept ringing. There were no price tags at all. They packed my dress and veil in cartons as big as coffins and my mother, spellbound, bought me another dress with layers of hand-sewn pink petals descending in a bell shape from waist to floor.

I liked shopping for clothes but took only a spectator's interest in the rest of the wedding arrangements. I woke late every morning and mother sat on my bed, reporting on fresh developments and making sure I drank the orange juice she had squeezed.

Mother had finally decided, after a wrangle with the florist, that my seven bridesmaids (the Carols, the Normas and three unwanted cousins) were going to carry pink sweetheart roses pinned to red velvet muffs instead of traditional bouquets. And Ida Bled's wedding present was already baked and ripening in her cold room — two hundred rolls of wedding strudel, made with turkish delight and walnuts, encased in crisp, flaky, white pastry that floated like silk.

The wedding plans were at the fever pitch and mother was whirling, phoning, arranging and negotiating.

But I wasn't as concerned with muffs or strudels as I ought to have been because I had a problem I couldn't tell mother.

I was unable to remember what Martin Manheim looked like.

I was at Eatons between the scarves and handbags when I first tried to conjure up Martin's face. I managed some dark hair like a cheap toupee and a police identikit face with the features drawn in. I stared hard at a McDonald tartan scarf, panicking, praying that a miracle would happen, like Christ's face appearing on St. Veronica's handkerchief while she walked the road to Calvary.

What did I know about Martin except that he wrote a lot about Gothic perpendicular in his letters?

Auntie Zora had to go to the Carnegie library to look up Gothic perpendicular in the encyclopedia and found that it had something to do with old churches in England. The family thought it best if Zora supervised our correspondence. Two years of St. John's High School was no insurance against illiteracy — even counting Mr.

Gillespie's English classes where I read Sherlock Holmes stories aloud, in unison with the other boys and girls. (Mr. Gillespie was certain this infusion of Conan Doyle would increase our grammar comprehension levels.) Martin, who had successfully passed examinations at Berkeley, Harvard and Oxford, might be able to detect my spelling mistakes and know a subject from a predicate. Zora, at least, had not the benefit of Mr. Gillespie's teaching.

As I turned over the plaid scarf, wondering whom I was marrying, a kind of miracle did take place. Zora walked by.

It wasn't really such a coincidence because Zora spent practically every afternoon of her life traipsing the cold half mile on Portage Avenue between Eaton's and the Bay, keeping an eye out for friends and enemies as well as marked down goods.

Zora was cheerful.

"I'm going upstairs to the Grill Room to meet that Mrs. Zelchuk who looks like death warmed over. The income tax swooped down upon her husband and took away the books. He'll go to jail," she said with satisfaction. "Come on up. I'll treat you to some asparagus and cheese rolls."

Not even the prospect of seeing Mrs. Zelchuk in extremity while I ate, appealed.

I blurted out my trouble.

"Auntie Zora, I don't remember Martin Manheim's face. How can I marry a man when I don't know what he looks like? Tell mother to postpone the wedding. Or maybe call it off completely. I'll send back all the presents myself. Mother won't have to do a thing."

Zora was calm and put her arm around my shoulder.

"It's too late, Verna. Ida Bled's already made the strudel. You can't send them back. God, you're a foolish girl. Looks in men don't count. Grab Martin with or without a face while he's in the marrying mood. If you backtrack now, he'll be leavings for an English girl with bad teeth. I know what you're going through. It happens to everyone. Even me. I was married to your Uncle Gerald eight years when he joined the air force. I couldn't remember his face a week after he shipped out."

I was comforted by her experience and relaxed enough to go upstairs to the Grill Room and gloat over Mrs. Zelchuk.

Although I never did fill in the features of Martin's face until he returned two days before the wedding, Zora had eased my anxiety a little. I began to pay more attention to one of mother's biggest decisions: choosing the caterer for the wedding.

Henya Smetanya and Mrs. Zipper were the old-fashioned, north end caterers and at first, loyalty pulled mother in their direction. She was afraid that if she didn't pick one of them her north end friends would accuse her of snobbery, and Zora would attack her with "pseudoism" and betraying roots. But there was Mendel Glow to mull over, the south end caterer, who certainly would have been the first choice of Flora Manheim and her smart friends.

Henya and Mrs. Zipper were the cheapest but the important fact was that they specialized in north end delicacies — cabbage rolls, knishes, noodle puddings and half roast chicken. Aficionados of north end catering considered it to be at its peak if the plate was so crowded that the knish nudged the cabbage roll over the side of the plate onto the tablecloth, at the intrusion of the eager fork.

South enders, especially those who had lived there more than ten years, considered plate overload a vulgar ethnic syndrome, lacking refinement and aesthetics.

As Mendel Glow, the south end caterer, remarked, "Knishes, kugle, holupchi, kasha, who wants to look at four brown things on a plate?"

Mendel was a latecomer in the catering scene who

had cast a spell upon the south end ladies because he was a man. ("A capon," my father snorted.)

Innovative, Mendel offered egg rolls instead of cabbage rolls, "better than any Chinaman can make," and substituted the half roast chicken with "Individual Cornish Hen." (At a south end function, my father would sigh, "I hate those two shrivelled legs sticking into my face.")

Mendel's major achievement, "color contrast," was as revolutionary in its way as Giotto's discernment of space in the quattrocento. Just as early Renaissance Florentines began to appreciate and demand painting with dimension, the south end elites' aesthetic perceptions were radically enriched by strands of red pimento in the coleslaw, green tinted pears, and scooped out oranges filled with rice (still brown, however), ornamenting the main course plate.

This revolutionary drive for more and more color lagged far behind in the north end caterers' sensibilities. They were elderly women, with swollen varicosed legs, and tired eyes. While Mendel never cooked himself, the Henya Smetanyas and Mrs. Zippers were constantly keeling the pot. If you wanted to talk to them about the menu, let alone color contrast, you had to go to their messy kitchens and reason with them while they shook the kasha grains in the frying pan or poured boiling water over cabbage leaves. Mendel was more expensive but he had an office with a desk and engaged in relaxed conversation about sponge cake swans for dessert, never before seen in the city.

Zora claimed that Mendel took himself for Mr. Foy, the interior decorator at Eaton's, except that Mendel had a model of a wedding cake on his display table instead of fabric swatches. Zora disliked Mendel's family who had lived next door to Gerald's mother.

"Dirty, ignorant, and boorish. They ate cold salami for breakfast. Mendel had his first hot meal at Salisbury

House when he was eighteen. Their house stank like an abbatoir because Mrs. Glow kept live chickens in the summer kitchen. We complained three times to the sanitary inspectors."

Auntie Zora had no right to criticize Mendel Glow.

In the first place, Zora hated cooking — her canned tomato soup was always lumpy because "stirring is boring." And Zora never used a caterer in her life. When she had a party, my mother did the cooking. But she loved to visit the caterers and chat about possibilities. Surprisingly, Zora didn't urge mother to pick one of the north end caterers.

"Fanny, if I were having my big-bang-blow-out," she advised, "I'd aim for the stars. I think you should seriously consider the Alex. I don't care if they refused Lena Horne a room, they make the finest breakfast rolls from here to the South Dakota border."

She meant the Royal Alexandra Hotel, at the corner of Higgins and Main.

"Listen to me, Fanny. The Alex has the best trained waiters, with tail coats. Those fellows know how to handle the big silver soup tureens without clanging them around like a pair of cymbals. If Emelia Stone was giving the wedding, I bet she'd choose the Alex."

Daddy gave Zora the horselaugh.

"I thought you socialists hated the CPR. Where are your principles? You wanted to organize a picket when that Lena Horne thing happened."

Zora ignored Daddy.

"I just want to see your daughter get married in good taste. And what do you know about that?"

Mother kept her head and realized that a function at the Royal Alex would put the family in debt. Ronnie's medical education wasn't finished; he had three more years to go before his degree.

Mrs. Manheim, however, was breathing "south end"

in mother's ear and she felt she had to make a concession to the groom's side.

Mendel Glow was chosen caterer.

At first, mother didn't know whether to have a stand-up reception or a sit-down dinner, or a semi-buffet (stand-up to get the food and sit-down to eat it), at respectively $4.95, $5.95, or $6.95 a head.

And should she have shrimps or pickerel cheeks?

Mendel Glow gave clear advice.

"Shrimps aren't kosher but the stomach has no religion. Fanny, if you're having a lot of south enders, remember their shrine is a bowl of shrimp. But if the function has a heavy dose of north end people, double the amount of bread."

After father borrowed money from the bank, mother chose the sit-down, pickerel cheek, extra bread and sponge cake swan dinner, hoping the swans would appease the opposite forces — Flora Manheim and her brigade of south end friends.

The invitation list was another problem. Mother didn't know whom to leave out without feeling guilty. She was giving the biggest function in her life. (Functions were what Winnipeggers called important receptions — weddings, golden anniversaries, and bar mitzvahs. Mendel even used the word on his match boxes — "We cater the most pretentious functions".)

If mother was not able to face those whom she left out of her small luncheon affairs, it was impossible for her to stroke a name from the wedding list without feeling that she was subjecting the most remote acquaintance to abuse. Mother's guilt, combined with Flora Manheim's "musts" (relatives, friends, bond-drivers who would never speak to her again if they were not invited to her only son's wedding) pushed up the number of guests to several hundred.

At first mother feared a takeover by the Manheim

network. But she was able to put together a substantial if eclectic list. It encompassed, in addition to all available relations, most of Zora's CCF mailing list and such people as Mr. Shimkin, the vegetable man, who had given me a free watermelon every year on my birthday and Mr. Kingsley-Peel, president of Empire Seed and my father's boss, and his wife.

Daddy hadn't wanted the Kingsley-Peels at the wedding and would certainly have vetoed them if Kingsley-Peel hadn't invited himself.

Father and Mr. Kingsley-Peel were content with each other but normally they did not exchange social invitations. Mr. Kingsley-Peel was upper class Winnipeg, Manitoba Club, Winter Club, and lived on Roslyn Road. Father would as soon have asked Mr. Kingsley-Peel to a party as Mr. Lee, Noreen's Chinese father, who was again serving hot chicken sandwiches at the Bide a Wee café after the failure of Rex's restaurant. Father was happy with his social niche in the city and did not wish to budge, up or down.

But about a week before the wedding, Mr. Kingsley-Peel summoned my father to his office and congratulated him. "When you marry a daughter, a hump is off your back" is a backward ethnic saying, but Kingsley-Peel understood it, right to his Anglo-Saxon family compact soul. He had three unmarried daughters, "all up to no good," he told father.

"You're a lucky man, Sidney, hope the fellow your girl is marrying won't depend on you for money."

Then for the first time in a decade, he surprised father.

"I don't suppose Mrs. Kingsley-Peel and I could come? We've never been to a Jewish wedding. They tell me you people have a bun fest."

The Kingsley-Peels thus became two of the five hundred guests invited to my sit-down-dinner wedding.

The special molds arrived from Chicago for Mendel's swans.

Ronnie had begun the first draft of his master-of-ceremonies speech.

Ida Bled, at the last moment, said she would make her famous almond cornucopia for the sweet table — to be served late in the evening for those who wanted something extra with their coffee.

And I managed to put Martin Manheim and the thought of becoming a wife out of my mind until a week before the wedding.

I was standing outside Holt Renfrew, holding a large box containing another cocktail dress mother thought I might need for functions in Oxford, when Kenny walked by.

My contacts with Kenny had dwindled partly because of his suspicious relationship with Rabbi Ripp and partly because any conversation I had with him on campus was always monitored by Norma Bled. I hadn't seen him at all since I stopped going to university.

"Is that your wedding gown, Verna?"

This was the first time I heard him speak of my marriage. I felt ill. Perhaps I was right in the first place and Kenny was afflicted with shyness, not perversion. Perhaps he had always been in love with me. I wanted to drop the box, throw my arms around him and tell him that my wedding was a caper, a farce which I would immediately cancel if only he'd ask.

"It's just an ordinary dress." I answered.

"When does it happen?"

I hadn't asked Kenny to the wedding because I didn't want to see him when I walked down the aisle.

"December 20, at six o'clock."

"It seems like everyone's going to your wedding except me."

Two powerful, contradictory feelings of guilt gripped

me. I was marrying Martin Manheim instead of Kenny; and I hadn't asked him to the wedding. I wasn't sure which guilty feeling took priority over the other.

If only Kenny would give a sign like, "Verna, forget about Martin Manheim and wait for me. In eight years I'll have my Ph.D. in psychology."

Instead Kenny said, "You've surprised us all, Verna. I thought you were different. When Rabbi Ripp spoke about our archetypal foundations and the inherent barbarism of bourgeois civilization, your eyes always seemed to sparkle. I never would have guessed that all you really wanted was a wedding. So you're just going to be a housewife like Carol. I'll certainly miss seeing you in your wedding dress."

I remembered when Norma Bled and I used to make fun of Popular Carol's bourgeois goals. Now I was the hypocrite who had accepted the first man who sort of asked me (Harvey didn't count). I knew how contemptible I appeared to the Ripp-Kenny-Bled group. I wanted to tell Kenny that my wedding meant as much to me as turnips. But I couldn't.

Instead, I stood there thinking of Norma Bled. She was keen about labor unions and welfare systems and liked worrying about the atomic bomb. Rabbi Ripp had given Norma and me a copy of George Bernard Shaw's *An Intelligent Woman's Guide to Socialism*. I read a page, realized it wasn't funny like Pygmalion and went no further. Norma wrote a three thousand word analysis which Ripp-Kenny said was as good as anything Beatrice Webb might have done.

I knew I didn't care about politics — just failure. I was so afraid of failing exams, being fired from jobs, going away alone. Marriage had to be my solution. It meant success to Zora and my parents, if not to Kenny, Ripp, or Bled.

I accepted Kenny's disdain as just; but I suspected he wasn't entirely honest in his motives. Kenny was young and dependent on Ripp just as I felt I was dependent on M. M. Perhaps Kenny was disgusted with me because I had deserted his kind of political thinking. Perhaps he was in love with me. But perhaps there was a third motive. He might simply be angry because he hadn't been invited to my big-bang-blow-out. Kenny was too mysterious for me, intellectually as well as physically.

My other sense of guilt, Fanny's guilt, took over.

"Would you like to come to the wedding? Norma Bled and a lot of others you know will be there. We're going to dance after the meal."

I realized my invitation was cruel if he loved me. But if he didn't it was rude not to ask him.

"Sure I'll come. What do you want for a wedding present?"

Before I answered, he walked away.

15
The Hump
is Removed

Ronnie's nickname for me was Vacillation Verna.

If I had stopped the wedding plans one day I'd regret my decision the next. I couldn't imagine what my life would be like after the wedding. But I had a pretty good idea what would be in store if I didn't see it through.

Marriage to Caligula would be preferable to facing the consequences of a cancellation.

The thought of living with a stranger had less meaning for me than the wedding day. It would be outrageous if I didn't show up in my champagne lace wedding dress on December 20, 6:00 p.m., just because I had a soft spot for Kenny.

The advantage of a big wedding was that worries about administration and protocol took precedence over personal anxiety. There were serious matters to resolve; the most serious a confrontation with Mendel Glow over Millie Moss' present, and the seating of Noreen.

Millie was giving me 750 cabbage rolls, meant to be eaten at my wedding dinner.

Mendel Glow called cabbage rolls "greenhorn garbage." Mendel's proposed switch from Russian cabbage rolls (holipchi) to Chinese egg rolls had no political overtones in the international sense, but the factions between north and south end had to be taken into account.

Millie Moss — a north end loyalist — felt there was a limit to which mother could pander to south end refinements — and the limit stopped at cabbage rolls. Millie told mother her integrity as a north ender was in question because Mendel offered tinted peaches, scooped out oranges, and cornish hens, but not one round brown thing.

On the pretext that she was saving face for mother, Millie decided to make the holipchi herself. She drove Joe's old truck to the market, loaded the back with picked cabbages, commandeered all the boiling and roasting pots in their neighborhood, took the phone off the hook and began to wrap the big ribbed leaves around 30 pounds of ground chuck.

Cabbage stink hung over the whole north end but only the few not invited to the wedding complained.

Millie brought the cabbage rolls to our house the night before the wedding. Mother had been expecting their appearance but had been afraid to forewarn Mendel. After Millie left, Daddy insisted that she flush them down the toilet. Cabbage gave him gas and that is where they belonged. But mother knew Millie would never forgive her and called Zora for help.

"You have no choice, Fanny. Shlep them to Mendel. Maybe if you explain that he could serve the cabbage rolls separately from the rest of his food, the south enders won't think he made them. Mendel won't put them on his main course plate anyhow. The color planes would overlap and they'd ruin his minimal grouping."

Zora loved using Mendel's lingo.

"If you don't serve the cabbage rolls — watch out! Millie Moss will curse you. And then, God forbid, you'll end up with someone spitting prune pits in your eyes. Widows' curses always hold."

Zora offered to carry the twenty pots and pans to Mendel on the morning of my wedding. "Fanny, you know I help you with the dirty work when it comes to the crunch."

After Mendel finally understood that Zora really wanted them served at the wedding, he was surprisingly gracious. He smiled as a paternalistic anthropologist might when an aborigine who, with the best will in the world, presented him with a gift of sheep dung. As an objective scientist, Mendel understood that the revolting objects were of sacred importance to the primitives of the north end jungles.

Only for a second did the more natural response, nausea, reveal itself upon his face.

The seating of Noreen was never really solved to anyone's satisfaction. Noreen had been Rex's girlfriend for fifteen years. But was she family? Mother had not treated her as Rex's wife when she sent out the invitations. Married couples shared one stamp, two vellum envelopes and one embossed card but mother had sent Noreen and Rex separate invitations.

Rex was no help with the seating of Noreen. He played a devious role, allowing Noreen to believe that she would be at the head table with him and the other close relations, yet telling my mother, "Noreen's going to sit with the real aunts over my dead body. We are not married." Rex was not my real uncle either but mother said that since my grandmother had brought him up, he should be classified as such.

People that we had never met before, like Martin's weird aunt from Minot, North Dakota, had a seat at the head table, admittedly the extreme left end. Since her arrival, this aunt had stood outside the bathroom of whatever house she was in, guarding the door. She never spoke but stared hard at all those who entered and left. My father believed that her behavior exposed a recessive gene in Martin's family. "Fanny," he whispered to mother, hoping that I wouldn't overhear, "Verna's children might be imbeciles."

Whatever his doubts about my fiancé's family's genetic make-up, he never tried to stop the wedding; it was sufficient that mother share his worries.

Two days before the delivery of the cabbage rolls and in between placatory phone calls to Noreen, M. M. returned from Oxford. We both were so busy that we could only nod to each other in passing but managed a chat during the rehearsal. Once M. M. came to the house to view the wedding presents. He picked up a silver angel cake slicer (Emelia Stone's gift) and said it looked like a comb for a gorilla.

That was the limit of our intimacy.

On December twentieth, shortly after 7 p.m., at the age of eighteen, I married a stranger. M. M. was not responsible. Neither was I. Over the past months, the wedding had grown into a large bureaucratic undertaking. Our jobs were prestigious, but we lacked power — we could only follow orders. I was convinced the wedding had become a permanent institution, which would continue to function when M. M. and I left Winnipeg.

After the ceremony, we shook hands with five hundred people and seated ourselves at the head table. I was placed to the left of the wedding cake and the right of the carnations, so that the guests' view of me would not be blocked. I thought I was going to vomit in front of everyone and concentrated on avoiding catastrophe.

My head was bowed and my mouth closed — a desirable pose for a modest bride.

The head table was on a platform. Below and beyond was the first row of round tables for the exclusive use of the first cousins, nephews, nieces, and second cousins from out-of-town. The second row was for friends and local distant relations and behind them were the tables for paybacks, people who did not fit into the former categories but who had asked either set of parents to im-

portant functions. At the farthest distance from the head
table, where Noreen was forced to sit, were the odds and
ends.

Odds and ends were Edna, Mr. Manheim's secretary,
a tiger in the office but a giggler socially, Mr. Shimkin the
fruit man, and Anka whose twitching increased ten-fold
at grand functions. Noreen sat between Anka and the
Kingsley-Peels (mother had seen to that). And finally there
was Kenny.

Martin's toast to the bride was not well received.

He thanked his parents for giving him a wonderful
education, he spoke of his grandfather, a remarkable man
who had created the first bowling alley in Crystal City,
Manitoba, and his father, also a wonderful man who
owned a firm that supplied bathroom roller towels in commercial buildings throughout western Canada. He asked
everyone to stand and raise a glass in honor of his mother,
peerless hostess and charity worker.

Zora was outraged. She clanged her glass with a fork
in the middle of Martin's speech, looking, my brother told
me, like a thwarted Katisha who just heard she wasn't
getting Nanki Poo. Zora was wearing a long dress with
kimono sleeves and a thick purple cummerbund, with her
hair, as usual, knotted on top of her head, the tortoiseshell
pins that held it sticking out like deadly needles. A
Japanese demon goddess in her wrath, Zora stood up and
interrupted Martin.

"The first toast belongs to our side. I drink to the
family who paid for this wedding and to the bride who is
no slouch."

My father, easily excited like his sister Zora, and
hard of hearing, thought Martin had positively refused to
toast the bride. He rose and said that the wedding would
go no further, he was calling it off.

My brother suddenly realized he was toastmaster,
stood up and told everyone to sit down.

Martin, chagrined, rose, apologized and offered a

toast to the bride, "one of the prettiest girls in the city."

Rex stood up and roared, "One of the prettiest, you educated fool, she's the most beautiful."

Martin gibbered, "the most beautiful, Winnipeg's Aphrodite, Venus of the Province, Princess of the Prairies."

Zora lifted her glass, pushed my father down in his seat as Rex's point was taken, and our side drank. My father-in-law, a conciliatory man, suggested to my mother that the four-piece band strike up the Anniversary Waltz.

If it wasn't for Mr. Shimkin's conversation at the odds and ends table, Noreen might have taken her seat in the bleachers with better grace. Mr. Shimkin, who had a certain professional interest at stake, grumbled all evening because there were sponge cake swans instead of fruit salad for dessert.

"None of these people at the wedding eat enough fruit," he confided to Noreen. "Even a nice young girl like you has bad color."

Noreen, made low by Mr. Shimkin's conversation and her placement so far from Rex, walked around during the dancing and drank up the dregs of whiskey from the glasses on the tables. Fortified, she at first latched onto Kingsley-Peel cheek to cheek, thigh to thigh, and pushed him around the dance floor, leaving Mrs. Kingsley-Peel to continue the dialogue with Mr. Shimkin about fruit.

Rex was so embarrassed he avoided her all evening and spent his time with Emelia Stone describing his family tree and its noble Scottish branches.

Kenny had liked Noreen when they worked together at the House of Norograd. At the wedding he saw her as a Balzacian heroine, destined to be trodden upon by the bourgeois Mr. Kingsley-Peel, and driven to alcohol by Rex, the social climbing lover. She was the classic fallen heroine, born of mixed blood.

Kenny was ready to put political theory to action.

Ignoring Norma Bled, with her red muff covered with

sweetheart roses, he cut into Noreen's waltz with Kingsley-Peel and then danced all evening with her.

Millie Moss, who realized Martin was upset about the reaction to his speech, sat down beside him and spoke of the happy future, our honeymoon. Mr. Manheim's wedding present was two first-class tickets on the *Christoforo Columbo*, the flag ship of the Italian line, and a week at the San Domenico Hotel in Taormina in Sicily.

Millie was, of course, in charge of arrangements.

"It's the first time I ever heard of anyone going to Sicily on purpose. Those people that live there are all leaving. Haven't you heard? And going on an Italian boat. That's crazy too. You might think you're going to Naples but you'll probably end up in Hong Kong. Italians aren't good at driving boats. Everyone knows when they shipwreck the crew saves themselves first. By the way, did you like my holipchi? I made one-and-a-half for each guest. They're good luck at weddings."

Ronnie said everything else went fairly smoothly. Except that Noreen and Kenny left together.

When Rex found out he abandoned Emelia Stone and drove after them in his Rolls Royce.

And mother was annoyed at Mendel. After all her effort to accommodate south end taste buds, nearly everyone left their sponge cake swans untouched on the plate.

And everyone ate the cabbage rolls.

Epilogue

A week after my wedding, Noreen and Kenny took a bus to Los Angeles and got married.

Kusy Gwertzman went with them and the three lived together there for ten years. Kusy made money gambling in Las Vegas and bought a dairy, which Kenny managed.

The ménage-à-trois broke up when Kusy realized the potential of yoghurt earlier than the other California dairies and became rich.

Noreen and Kenny divorced and she got enough alimony to get onto art gallery and symphony committees in the manner of Emelia Stone.

Kenny and Kusy stayed with the dairy business and remained single. Each built a house by the sea in Malibu.

Rex disappeared for a while when Noreen left but came back to build the dream of his life, a big apartment block on the Assiniboine River called The Lord Rex. It filled up immediately so he built another across the street, called The Lord Rex West. He never married and his hobby is grafting apple trees in the orchard of his Lockport Lodge.

Rex is looking for the perfect hybrid, tart yet sweet and crunchy, with a long counter life and not too small. So far he has been unsuccessful.

Norma Bled took an MA in social work and during the sixties lived in Labrador with a man who had a federal grant to film the interfaces of Eskimos and the white communities. She wrote to me, explaining what that meant:

"When the native people see themselves in the movie, buying tea and corn syrup, their perception of themselves will go through a radical change. Then they'll knock off the storekeeper."

I don't know if they call parties functions or affairs in Winnipeg now. There was a wedding reception jointly catered by Henya Smetanya and Mrs. Zipper, their last big catering job for they both died in harness, true to their art, six months afterward. And now cabbage rolls are no longer served at the big affairs.

Mendel Glow's coloristic theories are no longer unique. Other caterers from the north and south end can equal his work with tinted peaches. But Mendel remains innovative. He has lately sent out a folder advertising bean sprouts instead of coleslaw and a coating of wheat germ on the Cornish Hen.

Auntie Zora has given up on the conversaziones. She explained to mother, "I caught them nodding through Thomas Mann."

She bought a fondue pot for late evening entertaining but discontinued it in 1970 at the dawning of the age of cholesterol. She insists that yoghurt dips and raw cauliflower be passed at affairs in all north end homes. She even wanted one of her NDP candidates to include this proposal in a campaign pamphlet as part of his preventative health platform.

Great Uncle Miller died in his house on Lancaster Street, much to my father's disgust. Father believed that the sick and dying belonged in hospital and to him death at home was unhygienic and "old country." Anka with her Raggedy Ann appearance and equally bedraggled mop, never followed hospital sanitary procedures. But she slept in a cot in Great Uncle's sick room, massaged and moved his body every hour, wrapped him in bread poultices and cupped his chest with whiskey shot glasses. She spared him the torture of needles and catheters — the painful paraphernalia of hospital death.

Great Aunt Miller had a fatal heart attack one month later with Anka at her side. The Lancaster house was left to Anka and she lived in it for many years until the zoning laws changed. Four houses on Lancaster were torn down and a dentists' building was erected. Everyone left on the street held their breath and hoped. And not in vain. A parking lot company offered Anka, Lila Wees, and five other house owners enough money to keep them in more comfort than Great Uncle Miller experienced during his life. Lila Wees was so excited she talked about getting into dry cleaning.

But Anka wouldn't sell.

"If they offer us so much, they'll give more if we wait. This is just the beginning. I wait."

One summer evening after the usual argument, Anka shook her fist at Lila, yelling, "I don't sell. I wait."

Then she fell backwards on her late August vegetables and died.

She left the house to Great Uncle Miller's children in the States who sold it immediately. And now there's another parking lot in the wrongie section of the north end.

Popular Carol remained popular. She married three times — each husband richer and more desirable than the last. Her latest is Iranian and they have no fixed home. As she says, "We're true nomads and unfold our tents in Claridges, the Paris Ritz and the Carlyle in New York."

Harvey returned to MIT and became a professor. His wife, a New England girl, is an entomologist and they have four children.

At the age of seventy, Emelia Stone married Rabbi

Ripp. His wife had divorced him not long after my wedding. He remained in the city, editing literary magazines which never prospered and lecturing part time at the university. Although there is twenty years between them, Emelia and Ripp appear pleased with each other. He convinced her to open an art gallery not too far from Lancaster Street. What they enjoy most are the buying trips.

The *Christoforo Columbo* did not shipwreck as Millie expected but we had trouble in Taormina. We arrived at the San Dominico on December 31 and the hotel was filled for New Year's Eve. Orange trees were blossoming in the courtyard, beautiful women in white cashmere, speaking many tongues, were drinking Fernet Branca in the garden. The concierge, in his cut away and grey silk ascot, recognized our name at once.

"Yes, excellency, we have your request for a room and a deposit. But unfortunately, your travel agent in Canada sent the letter sea mail. Look at the postage. It just arrived this morning. Of course, we have no room. But you can have your deposit back."

We skipped Sicily and went directly to Oxford.

I was pretty gauche. I didn't know that I was supposed to go to the bathroom with the other women after the savory at dinner parties so the men could drink port by themselves. They didn't do that in Winnipeg. It wouldn't have been so bad except that "after finding the geography of the house," the ladies would pick up newspapers and not talk to each other at all.

One day when M. M. and I were walking down High Street he pointed out a man whom he called "the real Oxford dregs."

"They had to sack him after thirty years. Practically an unheard of thing around here. And not just because he was an alcoholic. He refused to tutor any man who wasn't beautiful. Gave the tutorials from his bed when he was in Oxford. He'd disappear for months. Some say he used to go on profitable lecture tours to remote parts of America.

"When I went for my first and only tutorial, his room was filled with empty gin bottles and there were greening crumpets scattered about.

"He told me never to return when I said I came from Winnipeg."

It was Blythe Llewellyn Chaftit.

"Looks about ninety," M. M. observed. "Must be the booze."

"No," I answered. "It's because he doesn't eat tongue."

Mrs. Manheim was right. Oxford didn't suit Winnipeg girls.

A year later we came back to Canada and spent the next twenty-two years getting acquainted.